MW00606829

SkillBuilder

Grade 6

Math Workbook - 2

‣ *Expressions & Equations*
‣ *Geometry*

Important Instruction

Students, Parents, and Teachers can use the URL or QR code provided below to access additional practice questions, educational videos, worksheets, mobile apps, standards information and more.

URL	QR Code
Visit the URL below and place the book access code **http://www.lumoslearning.com/a/tedbooks** **Access Code: SBEEG6M-48517-P**	

Developed by Expert Teachers

Contributing Author - Renee Bade
Contributing Author - Kimberly Greacen
Executive Producer - Mukunda Krishnaswamy
Designer - Mirona Jova
Database Administrator - Sowmya R.

COPYRIGHT ©2018 by Lumos Information Services, LLC. ALL RIGHTS RESERVED. No part of this work covered by the copyright hereon may be reproduced or used in any form or by any means graphic, electronic, or mechanical, including photocopying, recording, taping, Web distribution or information storage and retrieval systems without the written permission of the publisher.

First Edition -2020

ISBN-10: 0-9820232-9-4

ISBN-13: 978-0-9820232-9-7

Printed in the United States of America

For permissions and additional information contact us

Lumos Information Services, LLC
Email: support@lumoslearning.com

PO Box 1575
Piscataway, NJ 08855-1575
Tel: (732) 384-0146
Fax: (866) 283-6471

http://www.LumosLearning.com

Lumos Learning
Developed by Expert Teachers

Lumos Expressions & Equations and Geometry Skill Builder, Grade 6 - Evaluating Expressions, Surface Area and Volume

This Book Includes:

- Practice questions to help students master
  ‣ Expressions & Equations
  ‣ Geometry
- Detailed Answer explanations for every question
- Strategies for building speed and accuracy

Plus access to Online Workbooks which include:

- Instructional videos
- Mobile apps related to the learning objective
- Hundreds of additional practice questions
- Self-paced learning and personalized score reports
- Instant feedback after completion of the workbook

Table of Contents

Additional Information

Online Program Benefits

Students*

- Rigorous Standards Practice
- Technology-enhanced item types practice
- Additional learning resources such as videos and apps

Parents*

- You can review your student's online work by logging in to your parent account
- Pinpoint student areas of difficulty
- Develop custom lessons & assignments
- Access to High-Quality Question Bank

Teachers*

- Review the online work of your students
- Get insightful student reports
- Discover standards aligned videos, apps and books through EdSearch
- Easily access standards information along with the Coherence Map
- Create and share information about your classroom or school events

* Terms and Conditions apply

URL	QR Code
Visit the URL below and place the book access code **http://www.lumoslearning.com/a/tedbooks** **Access Code: SBEEG6M-48517-P**	

Start using the online resources included with this book today!

Introduction

Books in the Lumos Skill Builder series are designed to help students master specific skills in Math and English Language Arts. The content of each workbook is rigorous and aligned with the robust standards. Each standard, and substandard, has its own specific content. Taking the time to study and practice each standard individually can help students more adequately understand and demonstrate proficiency of that standard in their particular grade level.

Unlike traditional printed books, this book provides online access to engaging educational videos, mobile apps and assessments. Blending printed resources with technology based learning tools and resources has proven to be an effective strategy to help students of the current generation master learning objectives. We call these books tedBooks™ since they connect printed books to a repository of online learning resources!

Additionally, students have individual strengths and weaknesses. Being able to practice content by standard allows them the ability to more deeply understand each standard and be able to work to strengthen academic weaknesses. The online resources create personalized learning opportunities for each student and provides immediate individualized feedback.

We believe that yearlong learning and adequate practice before the test are the keys to success on standardized tests. The books in the Skill Builder series will help students gain foundational skills needed to perform well on the standardized tests.

How to Use this Book Effectively

The Lumos Program is a flexible learning tool. It can be adapted to suit a student's skill level and the time available to practice. Here are some tips to help you use this book and the online resources effectively:

Students

- The standards in each book can be practiced in the order designed, or in the order of your own choosing.
- Complete all problems in each workbook.
- Use the online workbooks to further practice your areas of difficulty and complement classroom learning.
- Watch videos recommended for the lesson or question.
- Download and try mobile apps related to what you are learning.

Parents

- Get student reports and useful information about your school by downloading the Lumos StepUp® app. Please follow directions provided in "How to download Lumos StepUp® App" section of Lumos StepUp® Mobile App FAQ for Parents and Teachers.
- Review your child's performance in the "Lumos Online Workbooks" periodically. You can do this by simply asking your child to log into the system online and selecting the subject area you wish to review.
- Review your child's work in each workbook.

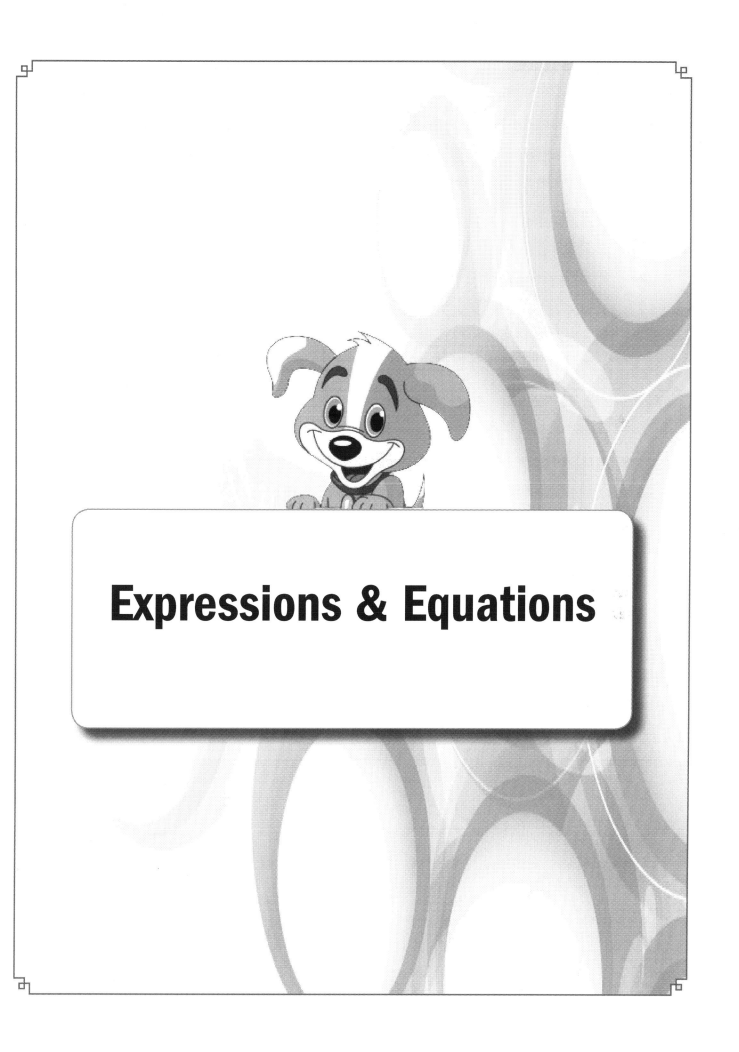

Expressions & Equations

Whole Number Exponents

1. **Evaluate: 5^3**

   Ⓐ 15
   Ⓑ 125
   Ⓒ 8
   Ⓓ 2

2. **Write the expression using an exponent: 2 * 2 * 2 * 2 * 2 * 2**

   Ⓐ 2 * 6
   Ⓑ 12
   Ⓒ 2^6
   Ⓓ 6^2

3. **Write the expression using an exponent: y * y * y * y**

   Ⓐ 4y
   Ⓑ y/4
   Ⓒ 4^y
   Ⓓ y^4

4. **Find the numerical value of the following expression: 11^1**

   Ⓐ 11
   Ⓑ 1
   Ⓒ 12
   Ⓓ 10

5. **Write an expression using exponents: 2 * 2 * m * m**

   Ⓐ 2(2m)
   Ⓑ 4m
   Ⓒ 2^2m^2
   Ⓓ 2/m

6. **Simplify: $4^3 * 4^2$**

   Ⓐ 20
   Ⓑ 9
   Ⓒ 4^5
   Ⓓ 20

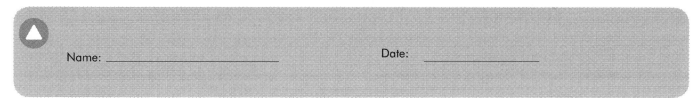
7. **Simplify: $(b^2c)(bc^3)$**

   Ⓐ 3b/4
   Ⓑ 3b * 4
   Ⓒ b^3c^4
   Ⓓ bc

8. **Simplify: $(n^4x^2)^3$**

   Ⓐ 12n*6x
   Ⓑ $n^{12}x^6$
   Ⓒ $n^{43}x^{23}$
   Ⓓ n^7x^5

9. **Simplify: $7^4/7^2$**

   Ⓐ 7^6
   Ⓑ 7^3
   Ⓒ 7^2
   Ⓓ 7^4

10. **Simplify: $[(3^5)(3^2)]^4$**

    Ⓐ 3^{28}
    Ⓑ 3^{40}
    Ⓒ 3^{10}
    Ⓓ 3^{11}

11. **Select all numbers that would have a total value greater than 50.**

    Ⓐ 6^2
    Ⓑ 2^3
    Ⓒ 5^2
    Ⓓ 10^2
    Ⓔ 4^4

12. Find the numerical value of 8^4. Write your answer in standard form in the box.

```
┌─────────────────────────────┐
│                             │
│                             │
└─────────────────────────────┘
```

Online Resources: Whole Number Exponents

URL	QR Code
http://lumoslearning.com/a/m15255	

 Videos   Apps   Sample Questions

NOTES

Expressions Involving Variables

1. When the expression 3(n + 7) is evaluated for a given value of n, the result is 33. What is the value of n?

   Ⓐ n = 4
   Ⓑ n = 5
   Ⓒ n = 21
   Ⓓ n = 120

2. Which number is acting as a coefficient in this expression? 360 + 22x – 448

   Ⓐ 360
   Ⓑ 22
   Ⓒ 448
   Ⓓ None of these

3. Evaluate the following when n = 7: 5(n – 5)

   Ⓐ 10
   Ⓑ –60
   Ⓒ 60
   Ⓓ 30

4. For which of the following values of b does the expression 4b – 9 have a value between 90 and 100?

   Ⓐ b = 104
   Ⓑ b = 26
   Ⓒ b = 48
   Ⓓ b = 24

5. Evaluate the following when n = –4: [5n – 3n] + 2n

   Ⓐ b = 16
   Ⓑ b = –20
   Ⓒ b = –16
   Ⓓ b = 0

6. **Translate the following: "Four times a number n is equal to the difference between that number and 10"**

   Ⓐ 4n = 10 − n
   Ⓑ 4 + n = 10*n
   Ⓒ 4/n = n + 10
   Ⓓ 4n = n − 10

7. **Evaluate 2y + 3y − y when y = 2.**

   Ⓐ 7
   Ⓑ 8
   Ⓒ 9
   Ⓓ 10

8. **Find the value of 2b − 4 + 6y when b = 2 and y = 3.**

   Ⓐ 16
   Ⓑ 18
   Ⓒ 0
   Ⓓ −12

9. **Translate the following, and then solve: "A number n times 16 is equal to 48."**

   Ⓐ 16n = 48, n = 4
   Ⓑ 16n = 48, n = 8
   Ⓒ 16 + n = 48, n = 32
   Ⓓ 16n = 48, n = 3

10. **For which value of x does 6x + 12 evaluate to 54?**

   Ⓐ x = 12
   Ⓑ x = 9
   Ⓒ x = 7
   Ⓓ x = 6

11. Circle the answer choice that represents "12 less than f".

Ⓐ 12 - f
Ⓑ (12)f
Ⓒ f - 12

12. Which of the following represents the phrase "the quotient of 17 and q"? Select all the correct answers.

Ⓐ q ÷ 17
Ⓑ 17 ÷ q
Ⓒ 17/q
Ⓓ q/17

Online Resources: Expressions Involving Variables

URL	QR Code
http://lumoslearning.com/a/m15249	

 Videos   Apps   Sample Questions

NOTES

Identifying Expression Parts

1. **Which of the following describes the expression 6(4−2) accurately?**

   Ⓐ Six and the difference of four and two.
   Ⓑ The product of six and the sum of four and two.
   Ⓒ The product of six and the difference of 4 and 2.
   Ⓓ The quotient of six and the difference of four and two.

2. **Which of the following describes the expression (8÷2)−10 accurately?**

   Ⓐ The quotient of eight and two subtracted from ten.
   Ⓑ Ten less than the quotient of eight and two.
   Ⓒ The difference of ten and the quotient of eight and two.
   Ⓓ The product of eight and two minus ten.

3. **What are the coefficients in the expression (2x + 15)(9x − 3)?**

   Ⓐ 2, 15, 9, −3
   Ⓑ 15, 3
   Ⓒ 15, −3
   Ⓓ 2, 9

4. **What is the value of the greatest coefficient in the expression $4a^2 + 9a − 11b^2 + 15$?**

   Ⓐ 4
   Ⓑ 9
   Ⓒ 11
   Ⓓ 15

5. **How many factors are in the following expression, 4(6 + 8) × 3(2 − 5)?**

   Ⓐ 2
   Ⓑ 4
   Ⓒ 5
   Ⓓ 6

6. Which of the following describes the expression $4 \div (5 \times \frac{1}{2})$ accurately?

   Ⓐ The quotient of 4 and $5\frac{1}{2}$

   Ⓑ divided by the quotient of 5 and $\frac{1}{2}$

   Ⓒ The quotient of 4 and the product of 5 and $\frac{1}{2}$

   Ⓓ The product of 5 and $\frac{1}{2}$ divided by 4.

7. Which of the following describes the expression $(6+9) - 4$ accurately?

   Ⓐ 4 subtracted from the sum of 6 and 9.
   Ⓑ The sum of 6 and 9 subtracted from 4.
   Ⓒ The difference of 6 and 9 less 4.
   Ⓓ The sum of the quantity of 6 plus 9 and 4.

8. Which term has the smallest coefficient in the expression $8x^4 + \frac{7}{8}x^3 - 2x^2 + x$?

   Ⓐ 1st term
   Ⓑ 2nd term
   Ⓒ 3rd term
   Ⓓ 4th term

9. Which of the following accurately represents "The product of 15 and the sum of 9 and 7."?

   Ⓐ $15 + (9 \times 7)$
   Ⓑ $(15 + 9) \times 7$
   Ⓒ $15 \div (9 + 7)$
   Ⓓ $15(9 + 7)$

10. Which of the following describes the expression $(12 \div 4) + [2 \times (-2)]$ accurately?

   Ⓐ The sum of the quotient of 12 and 4 and the product of 2 and −2.
   Ⓑ The quotient of 12 and 4 plus the difference of the product of 2 and 2.
   Ⓒ The quotient of 4 and 12 plus the product of 2 and −2.
   Ⓓ The difference of 2 times −2 and the quotient of 12 and 4.

11. **Which of the following means the same as 3(2+1)? Select all the correct answers.**

Ⓐ (2+1) + (2+1) + (2+1)
Ⓑ 6 + 3
Ⓒ 3 + 2 +1
Ⓓ (6 + 1) + (6 + 1) + (6 + 1)
Ⓔ None of the above

12. **_____ is the same as (3+1) + (3+1). Circle the correct answer choice.**

Ⓐ 2(3+1)
Ⓑ 3(2+1)
Ⓒ (3+1)²

Online Resources: Identifying Expression Parts

URL	QR Code
http://lumoslearning.com/a/m15258	

 Videos   Apps   Sample Questions

NOTES

Evaluating Expressions

1. **What is the value of y in the equation y = 3x – 13, when x = 6?**

   (A) 5
   (B) –4
   (C) –1
   (D) 4

2. **What is the value of y in the equation $y = \dfrac{1}{4} x \div 2$, when x = 32?**

   (A) 2
   (B) 4
   (C) 8
   (D) 10

3. **Evaluate the following expression when a = 3 and b = –8: $3a^2 – 7b$**

   (A) –44
   (B) –29
   (C) 68
   (D) 83

4. **Evaluate the following expression when v = –2 and w = 155: $6v^3 + \dfrac{4}{5} w$**

   (A) 17
   (B) 68
   (C) 76
   (D) 172

5. **Evaluate the following expression when c = –3 and d = 2: $\dfrac{6}{d} – 10c – c^4$**

   (A) –108
   (B) –48
   (C) 39
   (D) 114

6. Use the formula $V = s^3$ to find the volume of a cube with a side length of 2 cm.

    Ⓐ 4 cm²
    Ⓑ 6 cm³
    Ⓒ 8 cm³
    Ⓓ 9 cm³

7. Use the formula $A = l \times w$ to find the area of a rectangle with a length of 4.5 feet and a width of 7.3 feet.

    Ⓐ 28.15 ft²
    Ⓑ 30.35 ft²
    Ⓒ 32.35 ft²
    Ⓓ 32.85 ft²

8. Leah found a cylindrical container with a radius of $1\frac{1}{2}$ inches and a height of 11 inches. Use the formula $V = \pi r^2 h$, where $\pi = 3.14$, r is the radius and h is the height, to find the volume of the container. Round to the nearest hundredth.

    Ⓐ 51.81 in²
    Ⓑ 77.72 in²
    Ⓒ 103.62 in²
    Ⓓ 566.28 in²

9. What is the area of a square with a side of $\frac{3}{4}$ meter, $A = s^2$?

    Ⓐ $\frac{3}{16}$ m²

    Ⓑ $\frac{9}{16}$ m²

    Ⓒ $\frac{3}{4}$ m²

    Ⓓ $\frac{9}{4}$ m²

10. The area of the base of a square pyramid is 10 ft² and the height is 6 ft. What is the volume of the pyramid using the formula $V = \frac{1}{3}\beta h$, where β is the area of the base and h is the height?

    Ⓐ 20 ft³
    Ⓑ 60 ft³
    Ⓒ 200 ft³
    Ⓓ 600 ft³

11. Circle the answer that fits the 'x' in this equation $\frac{1200}{x} = 30$.

    Ⓐ 4
    Ⓑ 40
    Ⓒ 400

12. Select the equations in which j = 7. Choose all that apply.

    Ⓐ 3j – 4 = 25
    Ⓑ 56 – j = 49
    Ⓒ 3j + 4 = 25
    Ⓓ j³ = 343

Online Resources: Evaluating Expressions

URL	QR Code

http://lumoslearning.com/a/m15259

 Videos
 Apps
 Sample Questions

Name: _____   Date: _____

NOTES

Writing Equivalent Expressions

1. **What is an equivalent expression for 3n – 12?**

   Ⓐ 3n + 1
   Ⓑ 3n + 4
   Ⓒ 3n – 4
   Ⓓ 3(n – 4)

2. **Simplify 2n – 7n to create an equivalent expression.**

   Ⓐ 5n
   Ⓑ –5n
   Ⓒ –n(2 – 7)
   Ⓓ n(5)

3. **Which expression is equivalent to 5y + 2z – 3y + z?**

   Ⓐ z
   Ⓑ 2y + 3z
   Ⓒ yz
   Ⓓ 11yz

4. **Which expression is equivalent to 8a + 9 – 3(a + 4)?**

   Ⓐ 32 – 3a
   Ⓑ a
   Ⓒ 24a
   Ⓓ 5a – 3

5. **Which inequality has the same solution set as 3(q + 6) > 11?**

   Ⓐ 3q + 18 < 11
   Ⓑ 3q + 18 > 11
   Ⓒ 3q + 6 > 11
   Ⓓ q + 18 > 11

6. **Which inequality has the same solution set as 10 < q + q + q + q + q − 5?**

   Ⓐ 10 > 5q + 5
   Ⓑ 10 < 5q + 5
   Ⓒ 10 > 5q − 5
   Ⓓ 10 < 5q − 5

7. **Simplify the following equation:**
   u + u + u + u − p + p + p − r = 55

   Ⓐ 4u + 2p − r = 55
   Ⓑ 4u + p − r = 55
   Ⓒ 4u − 3p + r = 55
   Ⓓ 4u − 3p − r = 55

8. **36x − 12 = 108 has the same solution(s) as** _____ .

   Ⓐ 3(3x − 12) = 108
   Ⓑ 12(3x −1) = 108
   Ⓒ 3(12x − 12) = 108
   Ⓓ 12(x−1) = 108

9. **Why is the expression 5(3x + 2) equivalent to 15x + 10?**

   Ⓐ The 5 has been divided into each term in parentheses.
   Ⓑ The 5 was distributed using the Distributive Property.
   Ⓒ The 5 was distributed using the Associative Property.
   Ⓓ The expressions are not equal.

10. Which expression is equivalent to 5b − 9c − 2(4b + c)?

    Ⓐ −3b + 7c
    Ⓑ −3b − 7c
    Ⓒ −3b −11c
    Ⓓ −3b + 11c

11. Write the correct equation for the following expression. 3 less than the product of 4 and 5.

12. Circle the answer that represents 2(4+3b).

    Ⓐ 8 + 6b
    Ⓑ 6 + 8b
    Ⓒ 6b - 8

Online Resources: Writing Equivalent Expressions

URL	QR Code
http://lumoslearning.com/a/m15250	

 Videos   Apps   Sample Questions

NOTES

Identifying Equivalent Expressions

1. **Which two expressions are equivalent?**

   Ⓐ $(\frac{5}{25})x$ and $(\frac{1}{3})x$

   Ⓑ $(\frac{5}{25})x$ and $(\frac{1}{5})x$

   Ⓒ $(\frac{5}{25})x$ and $(\frac{1}{4})x$

   Ⓓ $(\frac{5}{25})x$ and $(\frac{1}{6})x$

2. **Which two expressions are equivalent?**

   Ⓐ $7 + 21v$ and $2(5 + 3v)$
   Ⓑ $7 + 21v$ and $3(4 + 7v)$
   Ⓒ $7 + 21v$ and $7(1 + 3v)$
   Ⓓ $7 + 21v$ and $7(7 + 21v)$

3. **Which two expressions are equivalent?**

   Ⓐ $\frac{32p}{2}$ and $17p$

   Ⓑ $\frac{32p}{2}$ and $18p$

   Ⓒ $\frac{32p}{2}$ and $16p$

   Ⓓ $\frac{32p}{2}$ and $14p$

4. **Which two expressions are equivalent?**

   Ⓐ $17(3m + 4)$ and $51m + 68$
   Ⓑ $17(3m + 4)$ and $51m + 67$
   Ⓒ $17(3m + 4)$ and $51m - 68$
   Ⓓ $17(3m + 4)$ and $47m + 51$

5. **Which two expressions are equivalent?**

    Ⓐ $\frac{64k}{4}$ and 4k

    Ⓑ $\frac{64k}{4}$ and 14k

    Ⓒ $\frac{64k}{4}$ and 16k

    Ⓓ $\frac{64k}{4}$ and 15k

6. **575d – 100 is equivalent to:**

    Ⓐ 25(23d – 4)
    Ⓑ 25(22d – 4)
    Ⓒ 25(23d + 4)
    Ⓓ 25(25d – 4)

7. **(800 + 444y)/4 is equivalent to:**

    Ⓐ 200 + 44y
    Ⓑ 800 + 111y
    Ⓒ 200 + 111y
    Ⓓ 200 – 111y

8. **5(19 –8y) is equivalent to:**

    Ⓐ 95 – 35y
    Ⓑ 95 + 40y
    Ⓒ 85 – 40y
    Ⓓ 95 – 40y

9. **The expression 3(26p – 7 + 14h) is equivalent to:**

    Ⓐ 78 – 21 + 42
    Ⓑ 78p + 21 + 42h
    Ⓒ 78p – 21 + 42
    Ⓓ 78p – 21 + 42h

10. 5(6x + 17y − 9z) is equivalent to:

    Ⓐ 30x + 82y − 45z
    Ⓑ 20x + 85y − 40z
    Ⓒ 30x + 85y − 45z
    Ⓓ 30x − 85y + 45z

11. Which of the following equations represents 4(2 + 1c)? Choose all that apply.

    Ⓐ 6 + 4c
    Ⓑ 6 + 5c
    Ⓒ 8 x 4c
    Ⓓ 8 + 4c
    Ⓔ (4 x 2) + (4 x 1c)
    Ⓕ (4 x 2) x (4 x 1c)

12. [(8y) + (8y) + (8y)] ÷ 2 = _____ . Simplify the expression and write the answer in the box.

> [   ]

Online Resources: Identifying Equivalent Expressions

URL	QR Code
http://lumoslearning.com/a/m15251	

 Videos   Apps   Sample Questions

NOTES

Equations and Inequalities

1. **How many positive whole number solutions (values for x) does this inequality have?**
   x ≤ 20

   Ⓐ 19
   Ⓑ 20
   Ⓒ 21
   Ⓓ Infinite

2. **Which of the following correctly shows the number sentence that the following words describe?** *17 is less than or equal to the product of 6 and q.*

   Ⓐ $17 \leq 6q$
   Ⓑ $17 \leq 6 - q$
   Ⓒ $17 < 6q$
   Ⓓ $17 \geq 6q$

3. **Which of the following correctly shows the number sentence that the following words describe?** *The quotient of d and 5 is 15.*

   Ⓐ $\dfrac{5}{d} = 15$

   Ⓑ $5d = 15$

   Ⓒ $\dfrac{d}{5} = 15$

   Ⓓ $d - 5 = 15$

4. **Which of the following correctly shows the number sentence that the following words describe?** *Three times the quantity u – 4 is less than 17*

   Ⓐ $3(u - 4) > 17$
   Ⓑ $3(u - 4) < 17$
   Ⓒ $3(u - 4) \leq 17$
   Ⓓ $3(u - 4) \geq 17$

5. **Which of the following correctly shows the number sentence that the following words describe?** *The difference between z and the quantity 7 minus r is 54.*

   (A) z − 7 − r = 54
   (B) z + 7 − r = 54
   (C) z + (7 − r) = 54
   (D) z − (7 − r) = 54

6. **Which of the following correctly shows the number sentence that the following words describe?** *The square of the sum of 6 plus b is greater than 10.*

   (A) $(6 + b)^2 > 10$
   (B) $6^2 + b^2 > 10$
   (C) $(6 + b)^2 = 10$
   (D) $(6 + b)^2 < 10$

7. **Which of the following correctly shows the number sentence that the following words describe?** *16 less than the product of 5 and h is 21.*

   (A) 16 – 5h = 21
   (B) 5h – 16 = 21
   (C) 16 – (5 + h) = 21
   (D) 16 < 5h + 21

8. **Which of the following correctly shows the number sentence that the following words describe?** *8 times the quantity 2x – 7 is greater than 5 times the quantity 3x + 9.*

   (A) 8(2x) – 7 > 5(3x) + 9
   (B) 8(2x – 7) ≥ 5(3x +9)
   (C) 8(2x – 7) > 5(3x + 9)
   (D) 8(2x – 7) < 5(3x + 9)

9. **A batting cage offers 8 pitches for a quarter. Raul has $1.50. Which expression could be used to calculate how many pitches Raul could get for his money?**

   (A) $1.50 x 8
   (B) $1.50 ÷ 8
   (C) ($1.50 ÷ $0.25) x 8
   (D) ($1.50 ÷ $0.25)

Name: _____   Date: _____

10. **For which of the following values of x is this inequality true?**

    500 − 3x > 80

    Ⓐ x = 140
    Ⓑ x = 150
    Ⓒ x = 210
    Ⓓ x = 120

11. **Circle the answer that correctly represents "d" in this equation.**

    3d + 4 > 17

    Ⓐ 5
    Ⓑ 2
    Ⓒ 4

12. **Select all values that could correctly represent b in the equation.**

    3b + 2 < 15

    Ⓐ 1
    Ⓑ 2
    Ⓒ 4
    Ⓓ 5
    Ⓔ 7

Online Resources: Equations and Inequalities

URL	QR Code
http://lumoslearning.com/a/m15252	

 Videos   Apps   📖 Sample Questions

NOTES

Modelling with Expressions

1. **Roula had 117 gumballs. Amy had x less than 1/2 the amount that Roula had. Which expression shows how many gumballs Amy had?**

   (A) $117 - x/2$
   (B) $(1/2)(117) - x$.
   (C) $117 - 2x$
   (D) $2x + 117$

2. **Benny earned $20.00 for weeding the garden. He also earned c dollars for mowing the lawn. Then he spent x dollars at the candy store. Which expression best represents this situation?**

   (A) $\$20 - c - x$
   (B) $\$20 + c - x$
   (C) $\$20 + c + x$
   (D) $\$20 + x/c$

3. **Clinton loves to cook. He makes a total of 23 different items. Clinton makes 6 different desserts, 12 appetizers, and x main courses. Which equation represents the total amount of food that Clinton cooked?**

   (A) $6 - 12 + x = 23$
   (B) $6 + 12 + x = 23$
   (C) $18 - x = 23$
   (D) $6 + 12 - x = 23$

4. **Simon has read 694 pages over the summer by reading 3 different books. He read 129 pages in the first book and he read 284 pages in the second book. Which equation shows how to figure out how many pages he read in the third book?**

   (A) $694 = 129 + 284 - y$
   (B) $694 = 413 - y$
   (C) $694 = 129 - 284 + y$
   (D) $694 = 129 + 284 + y$

5. Jimmy had $45.00. He spent all of the money on a hat and a pair of jeans. He spent $19.00 on the pair of jeans and x dollars on the hat. Which of the following equations is true?

    Ⓐ $45.00 + x = $19.00
    Ⓑ $45.00 − x = $19.00
    Ⓒ x − $19.00 = $45.00
    Ⓓ $19.00 + 45.00 = x

6. Janie had 54 stamps. She gave away t stamps. She then got back twice as many as she had given away. Which expression shows how many stamps Janie has now?

    Ⓐ 54 − t
    Ⓑ 54 + t
    Ⓒ 54 − 2t
    Ⓓ 2t − 54

7. The library has 2,500 books. The librarian wants to purchase x more books for the library. The director decides to buy twice as many as the librarian requested. How many books will the library have if the director purchases the number of books he wants?

    Ⓐ 2,500 + x
    Ⓑ 2,500 + 2x
    Ⓒ 2,500 − x
    Ⓓ 2,500 − 2x

8. There are 24 boys and 29 girls (not including Claire) attending Claire's birthday party. Which equation shows how many cupcakes Claire needs to have so that everyone, including herself, will have a cupcake?

    Ⓐ 24 − 29 = c
    Ⓑ 24 + 29 = c
    Ⓒ 24 + 30 = c
    Ⓓ 24 + c = 29

9. Heidi collects dolls. She had 172 dolls in her collection. Heidi acquired x more dolls from a friend. She then bought twice as many dolls from a yard sale. She now has 184 dolls in her collection. Which equation is true?

    Ⓐ 172 + 3x = 184
    Ⓑ 172 − x + 2x = 184
    Ⓒ 172(3x) = 184
    Ⓓ 172 − 3x = 184

10. Crystal grew 16 tomato plants. Each plant grew 10 tomatoes. She sold x of the tomatoes she had grown. Crystal has 54 tomatoes left for herself. Which equation is true?

Ⓐ 10(16 + x) = 54
Ⓑ 16(10 − x) = 54
Ⓒ 16 + x = 540
Ⓓ 160 − x = 54

11. Circle the answer that represents the statement 43 is greater than q correctly.

Ⓐ q > 43
Ⓑ 43 + q
Ⓒ 43 > q

12. Choose the box(es) that demonstrate that x is a number greater than 5. Choose all that apply.

Ⓐ x < 5
Ⓑ x > 5
Ⓒ x + 5
Ⓓ x - 5
Ⓔ 5 < x

Online Resources: Modeling with Expressions

URL	QR Code
http://lumoslearning.com/a/m15253	

 Videos   Apps   Sample Questions

NOTES

Solving One-Step Problems

1. Which of the following equations describes this function?

X	Y
13	104
17	136
20	160
9	72

- Ⓐ y = 18x
- Ⓑ y = x + 4
- Ⓒ y = x + 32
- Ⓓ y = 8x

2. What is the value of x?

− 7x = 56

- Ⓐ x = −7
- Ⓑ x = 8
- Ⓒ x = −49
- Ⓓ x = −8

3. Does this table show a linear relationship between x and y?

X	Y
13	169
15	225
12	144
	400
16	
7	
	64

- Ⓐ yes
- Ⓑ no
- Ⓒ yes, but only when x is positive
- Ⓓ yes, but only when y is a perfect square

4. **Find the value of z:** $\dfrac{z}{5} = 20$

   Ⓐ 100
   Ⓑ 4
   Ⓒ 15
   Ⓓ 25

5. **Find the value of y:** $\dfrac{y}{3} = 12$

   Ⓐ 9
   Ⓑ 15
   Ⓒ 36
   Ⓓ 4

6. **Find the value of p:** $13 + p = 39$

   Ⓐ 3
   Ⓑ 26
   Ⓒ 507
   Ⓓ 52

7. **Find the value of *w*:** $6w = 54$

   Ⓐ 48
   Ⓑ 60
   Ⓒ 324
   Ⓓ 9

8. **Find the value of *h*:** $h - 4 = 20$

   Ⓐ 24
   Ⓑ 16
   Ⓒ −80
   Ⓓ −5

9. **Find the value of p:** $72 + p = 108$

   Ⓐ p = 30
   Ⓑ p = 36
   Ⓒ p = 180
   Ⓓ p = 40

10. Find the value of n: 428 – n = 120

Ⓐ n = −548
Ⓑ n = 308
Ⓒ n = −308
Ⓓ n = 548

11. Circle the answer that represents m correctly in the equation 4m = 16.

Ⓐ m = 4
Ⓑ m = 3
Ⓒ m = 12

12. Select the equations in which k = 8. Select all the correct answers.

Ⓐ 3(6 + k) = 42
Ⓑ ((4) 7) / k =14
Ⓒ 8k – 4 = 60
Ⓓ 7(k / 2) =35

Online Resources: Solving One-Step Problems

URL	QR Code
http://lumoslearning.com/a/m15260	

 Videos   Apps   Sample Questions

NOTES

Representing Inequalities

1. **A second grade class raised caterpillars. They had 12 caterpillars. Less than half of the caterpillars turned into butterflies. Which inequality shows how many caterpillars turned into butterflies?**

   Ⓐ x < 6
   Ⓑ x > 6
   Ⓒ x ≤ 6
   Ⓓ x ≥ 6

2. **Elliot has at least 5 favorite foods. How many favorite foods could Elliot have?**

   Ⓐ 4
   Ⓑ 2
   Ⓒ none
   Ⓓ an infinite number

3. **Julie has a box full of crayons. Her box of crayons has 549 crayons and at least 8 of them are red. Which inequality represents how many crayons could be red?**

   Ⓐ x ≥ 549
   Ⓑ 8 ≥ x ≥ 549
   Ⓒ 8 ≥ x
   Ⓓ 8 ≤ x ≤ 549

4. **Five times a number is greater than that number minus 17 is represented as _____ .**

   Ⓐ 5x > x − 17
   Ⓑ x + 5 > x − 17
   Ⓒ 5x < x − 17
   Ⓓ 5x > x + 17

5. "A number divided by five minus five is less than negative four" is represented as _____ .

    Ⓐ 5x − 5 < −4
    Ⓑ x/5 − 5 < −4
    Ⓒ x/5 − 5 > −4
    Ⓓ x/5 − 5 < 4

6. "Three times the quantity of a number times six plus three is less than 27" is represented as _____ .

    Ⓐ 6x + 3 < 27
    Ⓑ 3(6)x + 3 < 27
    Ⓒ 3(6x + 3) < 27
    Ⓓ 6x + 3(3) < 27

7. How would x > 3 be represented on a number line?

    Ⓐ The number line would show an open circle over three with an arrow pointing to the left.
    Ⓑ The number line would show an open circle over three with an arrow pointing to the right.
    Ⓒ The number line would show a closed circle over three with an arrow pointing to the right.
    Ⓓ The number line would show a closed circle over three with an arrow pointing to the left.

8. Amy and Joey each have jellybeans. The amount Amy has is 3 times the amount that Joey has. There are at least 44 jellybeans between them. Which inequality would help you figure out how many jellybeans Amy and Joey each have?

    Ⓐ x + 3x ≥ 44
    Ⓑ 3x ≥ 44
    Ⓒ 3 + x ≥ 44
    Ⓓ x + 3x ≤ 44

9. Sandra is a lawyer. She is working on x number of cases. She gets 8 more cases to work on. She now has more than 29 cases that she is working on. Which inequality could be used to figure out how many cases Sandra is working on?

Ⓐ 8x > 29
Ⓑ x + 8 < 29
Ⓒ x + 8 > 29
Ⓓ x − 8 < 29

10. There are 25 beehives on a farm. There are the same number of bees in each hive. The total number of bees on the farm is greater than 800. Which inequality could be used to figure out how many bees are in each hive?

Ⓐ 25/x > 800
Ⓑ 25x < 800
Ⓒ 25x > 800
Ⓓ 25 + x > 800

11. Circle the answer that represents the inequality shown on the number line below.

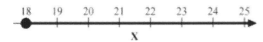

Ⓐ x ≥ 18
Ⓑ x < 18
Ⓒ x = 18

12. Choose the box that best represents the inequality on the line below.

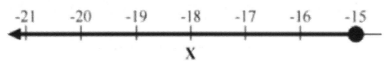

(A) x ≥ 15
(B) x ≥ -15
(C) x > -15
(D) x < -15
(E) x ≤ -15

13. A movie is rated PG13 meaning that one must be at least 13-years old to watch the movie. The sign in the lobby of the theater reads

> **PG13 Viewers**
> **must be ≤ 13**

Nami thinks the sign is wrong, but her friend Tai disagrees and finds nothing wrong with the sign. Who is correct and why?
Enter your answer in the box.

Name: _____   Date: _____

14. "A number divided by 5 is at most -23" is represented as _____.
Write the inequality and explain.

Online Resources: Representing Inequalities

URL	QR Code
http://lumoslearning.com/a/m15256	

 Videos   Apps   Sample Questions

NOTES

Quantitative Relationships

1. **Logan loves candy! He goes to the store and sees that the bulk candy is $0.79 a pound. Logan wants to buy p pounds of candy and needs to know how much money (m) he needs. Which equation would be used to figure out how much money Logan needs?**

   Ⓐ m = 0.79 ÷ p
   Ⓑ m = 0.79(p)
   Ⓒ 0.79 = m(p)
   Ⓓ m = 0.79 + p

2. **Logan is out of candy again! He goes to the store and sees that the bulk candy is now $0.84 a pound. Logan wants to buy 3 pounds of candy. Using the equation m = 0.84(p), figure out how much money (m) Logan needs.**

   Ⓐ $1.68
   Ⓑ $2.52
   Ⓒ $2.25
   Ⓓ $2.54

3. **Norman is going on a road trip. He has to purchase gas so that he can make it to his first destination. Gas is $3.55 a gallon. Norman gets g gallons. Which equation would Norman use to figure out how much money (t) it cost to get the gas?**

   Ⓐ t = g(3.55)
   Ⓑ t = g ÷ 3.55
   Ⓒ t = 3.55 ÷ g
   Ⓓ t = g + 3.55

4. **Norman needs to get gas again. This time, gas is $3.58 a gallon. Norman needs to get 13 gallons. Using the expression t = g(3.58), figure out how much Norman will spend (t) on gas.**

   Ⓐ $46.15
   Ⓑ $39.54
   Ⓒ $46.45
   Ⓓ $46.54

5. Penny planned a picnic for her whole family. It has been very hot outside, so she needs a lot of lemonade to make sure no one is thirsty. There are 60 ounces in each bottle. Penny purchased b bottles of lemonade. She wants to figure out the total number of ounces (o) of lemonade she has. Which equation should she use?

   Ⓐ b = 60(o)
   Ⓑ 60 = o ÷ b
   Ⓒ 60(b) = o
   Ⓓ 60 = b ÷ o

6. Ethan is playing basketball in a tournament. Each game lasts 24 minutes. Ethan has 5 games to play. Which general equation could he use to help him figure out the total number of minutes that he played? Let t = the total time, g = the number of games, and m = the time per game.

   Ⓐ t = g + m
   Ⓑ t = g(m)
   Ⓒ t = g − m
   Ⓓ t = g ÷ m

7. The Spencers built a new house. They want to plant trees around their house. They want to plant 8 trees in the front yard and 17 in the backyard. The trees that the Spencer's want to plant cost $46 each. Could they use the equation t = c(n) where t is the total cost, c is the cost per tree, and n is the number of trees purchased, to figure out the cost to purchase trees for both the front and the back yards?

   Ⓐ No, because the variables represent only two specific numbers that will never change.
   Ⓑ Yes, because the variables represent only two specific numbers that will never change.
   Ⓒ No, because the variables can be filled in with any number.
   Ⓓ Yes, because the variables can be filled in with any number.

8. Liz is a florist. She is putting together b bouquets for a party. Each bouquet is going to have f sunflowers in it. The sunflowers cost $3 each. Which equation can Liz use to figure out the total cost (c) of the sunflowers in the bouquets?

   Ⓐ c = 3(bf)
   Ⓑ c = bf ÷ 3
   Ⓒ c = 3b + f
   Ⓓ c = 3(b + f)

9. **Liz is a florist. She is putting together 5 bouquets for a party. Each bouquet is going to have 6 sunflowers in it. The sunflowers cost $3 each. Using the equation c = 3(bf), figure out how much Liz will charge for the bouquets.**

   Ⓐ $90
   Ⓑ $30
   Ⓒ $18
   Ⓓ $80

10. **Hen B (b) lays 4 times as many eggs as Hen A (a).**

Hen A	Hen B
2	8
4	16
7	28
11	44

   Which equation represents this scenario?

   Ⓐ b = 4 ÷ a
   Ⓑ b = 4 + a
   Ⓒ b = 4a
   Ⓓ b = 4a − 4

11. Which of the following represent balloons that have a cost of $2.50 for a quantity of 10? Choose all that apply.

Ⓐ 20 balloons cost $1.25
Ⓑ 100 balloons $25.00
Ⓒ 30 balloons cost $7.50
Ⓓ 80 balloons cost $8.00

12. Sodas cost $1.25 at the vending machine. Complete the table to show the quantity and total cost of sodas purchased.

Day	Money Spent on Sodas	Sodas Purchased	Price per Soda
Monday		24	$1.25
Wednesday	$57.50		$1.25
Friday	$41.25		$1.25

Online Resources: Quantitative Relationships

URL	QR Code
http://lumoslearning.com/a/m15257	

Videos   Apps   Sample Questions

End of Expressions & Equations

NOTES

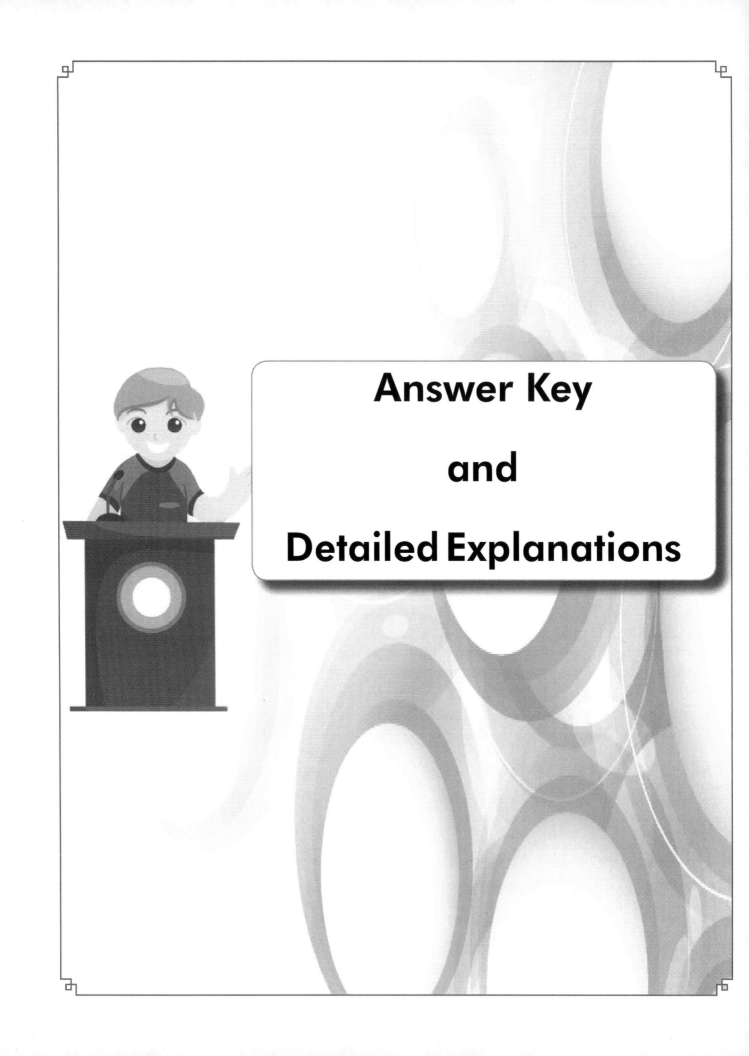

Answer Key

and

Detailed Explanations

Whole Number Exponents

Question No.	Answer	Detailed Explanations
1	B	The base is 5. The exponent is 3. 5 is multiplied 3 times, or 5 X 5 X 5 = 125
2	C	The base is 2. Count the factors. There are 6. 6 is the exponent. $2 * 2 * 2 * 2 * 2 * 2 = 2^6$
3	D	The base is y. Count the factors. There are 4. 4 is the exponent. $y * y * y * y = y4$
4	A	Write the factors: 11 Since 11 is the only factor, $11^1 = 11$
5	C	2^2m^2 The first base is 2. Count the number of 2s. There are 2. 2 is the exponent, so part of the expression is 2^2 The second base is m. Count the number of ms. There are 2. 2 is the exponent, so part of the expression is m^2 The full expression is written as: 2^2m^2
6	C	$4^3 * 4^2 = 4 * 4 * 4 * 4 * 4 = 4^5$
7	C	We know that $a^m * a^n = a^{(m+n)}$. Therefore, $(b^2c)(bc^3) = b^3c^4$
8	B	We know that $a^m * a^n = a^{(m+n)}$. Therefore, $(n^4x^2)^3 = n^{12}x^6$
9	C	We know that $a^m/a^n = a^{(m-n)}$. Therefore, $7^4/7^2 = 7^2$
10	A	$[(3^5)(3^2)]^4 = 3^{28}$ Keep the base the same. 3 is the base. Add the exponents inside the brackets. 5 + 2 = 7. The expression becomes $[3^7]^4$. To simplify further, multiply the exponents (since the base has a power raised to a power.) $[3^7]^4 = 3^{7*4} = 3^{28}$
11	D & E	D. $10^2 = 10 \times 10 = 100$ E. $4^4 = 4 \times 4 \times 4 \times 4 = 256$
12	4096	$8^4 = 8 \times 8 \times 8 \times 8 = 4,096$

Expressions Involving Variables

Question No.	Answer	Detailed Explanations
1	A	Since 3(n + 7) is equal to 33, then (n + 7) must equal 11 (3 x 11 = 33). Therefore, n must equal 4, since 4 + 7 = 11.
2	B	A number joined to a variable through multiplication is a coefficient. 22 is the coefficient of x.
3	A	When n = 7, the expression becomes 5(7 - 5) = 5 (2) = 10.
4	B	When b = 26, 4b − 9 = 4(26) − 9 = 104 − 9 = 95
5	C	When n = −4, the expression becomes: = [5(-4) − 3(-4)] + 2(-4) = [−20 − (−12)] − 8 = [−20 + 12] − 8 = [−8] − 8 = −16 Alternative Solution: [5n-3n]+2n = 2n + 2n = 4n = 4*(-4) = -16
6	D	Four times a number n means to multiply the variable n by 4, 4n. is equal to means = the difference between a number and 10 means to write the subtraction as is, from left to right, so n − 10. Therefore, 4n = n − 10
7	B	First, combine like terms: 2y + 3y − y = 4y Then, substitute 2 for y: 4(2) =8
8	B	Substitute 2 for b and 3 for y: 2(2) − 4 + 6(3) = 4 − 4 + 18 = 0 + 18 = 18
9	D	a number n times 16 is equal to 48 a number n times 16: 16n is equal to: = 16n = 48 n = 3, since 16(3) = 48
10	C	When x = 7, 6x + 12 = 6(7) + 12 = 42 + 12 = 54
11	C	f - 12, The phrase "12 less than f" indicates than f is being reduced, or subtracted, by the number 12.
12	B & C	B and C, The order of the numbers should match the phrase.

Identifying Expression Parts

Question No.	Answer	Detailed Explanations
1	C	$(4 - 2) \rightarrow$ The difference of 4 and 2. $6(4 - 2) \rightarrow$ The product of 6 and the difference of 4 and 2.
2	B	$(8 \div 2) \rightarrow$ The quotient of 8 and 2. $- 10 \rightarrow$ less 10 or 10 subtracted from. $(8 \div 2) - 10 \rightarrow$ 10 less than the quotient of 8 and 2.
3	D	A coefficient is the number multiplied by a variable. In this expression there are two variable terms, 2x and 9x. The coefficients are 2 and 9.
4	B	A coefficient is the number multiplied by a variable. In this expression there are three variable terms, $4a^2$, $9a$ and $-11b^2$. The coefficients are 4, 9, and -11. The value of the greatest coefficient is 9.
5	B	A factor is a term being multiplied by another term. In this expression we have four factors 4, (6+8), 3 and (2−5)
6	C	$(5 \times \frac{1}{2}) \rightarrow$ The product of 5 and $\frac{1}{2}$ $4 \div (5 \times \frac{1}{2}) \rightarrow$ The quotient of 4 and the product of 5 and $\frac{1}{2}$
7	A	$(6 + 9) \rightarrow$ The sum of 6 and 9 or 6 plus 9 $- 4 \rightarrow$ less 4 or 4 subtracted from $(6 + 9) - 4 = 4$ subtracted from the sum of 6 and 9
8	C	A coefficient is the number multiplied by a variable. In this expression there are four variable terms, $8x^4$, $\frac{7}{8}x^3$, $-2x^2$ and x. The coefficients are 8, $\frac{7}{8}$, -2 and 1. The value of the smallest coefficient is -2. Therefore the third term has the smallest coefficient.
9	D	The sum of 9 and 7 $\rightarrow$ (9 + 7) The product of 5 and the sum of 9 and 7 $\rightarrow$ 5(9 + 7)
10	A	$(12 \div 4) \rightarrow$ The quotient of 12 and 4 $+ \rightarrow$ sum $[2 \times (-2)] \rightarrow$ the product of 2 and -2 $(12 \div 4) + [2 \times (-2)] \rightarrow$ The sum of the quotient of 12 and 4 and the product of 2 and -2.
11	A & B	A. (2+1) + (2+1) + (2+1) B. 6 + 3
12	A	A number or an expression added to itself is twice the number or expression.

LumosLearning.com

Evaluating Expressions

Question No.	Answer		Detailed Explanations
1	A	$y = 3x - 13$	Original equation
		$y = 3(6) - 13$	Substitute 6 for x
		$y = 18 - 13$	Multiply
		$y = 5$	Subtract
2	B	$y = \frac{1}{4}x \div 2$	Original equation
		$y = \frac{1}{4}(32) \div 2$	Substitute 32 for x
		$y = \frac{32}{4} \div 2$	Multiply
		$y = 8 \div 2$	Simplify fraction
		$y = 4$	Divide
3	D	$3a^2 - 7b$	Original equation
		$3(3)^2 - 7(-8)$	Substitute 3 for a and −8 for b
		$3(9) - 7(-8)$	Exponents
		$27 - 7(-8)$	Multiply
		$27 - (-56)$	Multiply
		$27 + 56$	Change to adding
		83	Add
4	C	$6v^3 + \frac{4}{5}w$	Original equation
		$6(-2)^3 + \frac{4}{5}(155)$	Substitute −2 for v and 155 for w
		$6(-8) + \frac{4}{5}(155)$	Exponents
		$-48 + \frac{4}{5}(155)$	Multiply
		$-48 + 124$	Multiply
		76	Add
5	B	$\frac{6}{d} - 10c - c^4$	Original equation
		$\frac{6}{2} - 10(-3) - (-3)^4$	Substitute −3 for c and 2 for d
		$\frac{6}{2} - 10(-3) - (81)$	Exponents
		$3 - 10(-3) - (81)$	Divide
		$3 - (-30) - (81)$	Multiply
		$3 + 30 - (81)$	Change to adding
		$33 - (81)$	Add
		-48	Subtract

Question No.	Answer	Detailed Explanations	
6	C	$V = s^3$	Formula
		$V = s^3$	Substitute 2 for s
		$V = 8$ cm^3	Exponents
7	D	$A = l \times w$	Formula
		$A = 4.5 \times 7.3$	Substitute for l and w
		$A = 32.85$ ft^2	Multiply
8	B	$V = \pi r^2 h$	Formula
		$V = 3.14 \times (1.5)^2 \times 11$	Substitute the value for r and h (r=3/2=1.5)
		$V = 3.14 \times 2.25 \times 11$	Exponents
		$V = 77.715$	Multiply
		$V = 77.72$ in^3 rounding to two decimal places	
9	B	$A = s^2$	Formula
		$A = (\frac{3}{4})^2$	Substitute values
		$A = \frac{9}{16}$ m^2	Exponents
10	A	$V = \frac{1}{3} ßh$	Formula
		$V = \frac{1}{3}(10)(6)$	Substitute values
		$V = 20$ ft^3	Multiply
11	B	40, because 30 x 40 = 1200	
		Alternative Solution:	
		1200 / x = 30	
		x = 1200 / 30	
		x = 40	
12	B, C, & D	B. $56 - 7 = 49$	
		C. $3(7) + 4 = 25$	
		D. $7 \times 7 \times 7 = 343$	

Writing Equivalent Expressions

Question No.	Answer	Detailed Explanations
1	D	The expression, 3(n − 4), is equivalent because it has the same value as the original. The GCF (Greatest Common Factor) of 3 has been factored out from each term.
2	B	Here, the variable is the common factor and can be factored out n(2 − 7). Then, simplify within the parentheses: n(−5). Finally, use the Commutative Property to rewrite the expression, coefficient first: −5n.
3	B	5y + 2z − 3y + z = 2y + 3z Combine the like terms to simplify: 5y + 2z − 3y + z = (5y − 3y) + (2z + z) = 2y + 3z.
4	D	First use the Distributive Property to remove the parentheses: 8a + 9 −3(a +4) = 8a + 9 − 3a − 12 Then, combine like terms: 8a + 9 − 3a − 12 = (8a − 3a) + (9 − 12) = 5a + (−3) = 5a − 3
5	B	The Distributive Property states that a number outside of the parentheses should be used to multiply all numbers inside the parentheses. The inequality symbol should not change. The correct answer is 3q + 18 > 11
6	D	Combine like terms.: q + q + q + q + q = 5q Replace the simplified expression into the original inequality: 10 < 5q − 5
7	B	Combine like terms in the expression. u + u + u + u = 4u − p + p + p = p That makes the equation 4u + p − r = 55
8	B	The GCF of 36 and 12 is 12. The Distributive Property states that a number outside of the parentheses should be distributed to all numbers inside the parentheses. So, 36x − 12 = 108 can be rewritten as 12(3x − 1) = 108
9	B	The Distributive Property states that a number outside of the parentheses should be distributed to all numbers inside the parentheses. 5(3x +2) = (5*3x) + (5*2) = 15x + 10.

Question No.	Answer	Detailed Explanations
10	C	First use the Distributive Property to remove the parentheses: $5b - 9c - 2(4b + c) = 5b - 9c - 8b - 2c$ Then, combine like terms: $5b - 9c - 8b - 2c = (5b - 8b) + (-9c - 2c) = -3b + (-11c) = -3b - 11c$
11	(4 x 5) -3	(4 x 5) -3
12	A	8 + 6b The distributive property requires that 2 be multiplied by each quantity in parentheses, then the product of each is added. (2 x 4) + (2 x 3b) 8 + 6b

Identifying Equivalent Expressions

Question No.	Answer	Detailed Explanations
1	B	$(\frac{5}{25})$x and $(\frac{1}{5})$x are equivalent because $\frac{5}{25}$ simplifies to $\frac{1}{5}$. The expressions will be equivalent even if a number is substituted for x.
2	C	7 + 21v and 7(1 + 3v) are equivalent because if you distribute 7 to 1 +3v you will get 7 + 21v. The expressions will be equivalent even if a number is substituted for v.
3	C	32p/2 and 16p are equivalent because if you divide 32p by 2 you get 16p. The expressions will be equivalent even if a number is substituted for p.
4	A	17(3m + 4) and 51m + 68 are equivalent because if you distribute 17 to 3m + 4 you will get 51m + 68. The expressions will be equivalent even if a number is substituted for m.
5	C	64k/4 and 16k are equivalent because if you divide 64k by 4 you will get 16k. The expressions will be equivalent even if a number is substituted for k.
6	A	25(23d − 4) and 575d − 100 are equivalent because if you distribute 25 to 23d − 4 you will get 575d − 100. The expressions will be equivalent even if a number is substituted for d.
7	C	(800 + 444y)/4 and 200 + 111y are equivalent because if you divide 800 + 444y by 4 you will get 200 + 111y. The expressions will be equivalent even if a number is substituted for y.
8	D	5(19 − 8y) and 95 − 40y are equivalent because if you distribute 5 to 19 − 8y you will get 95 − 40y. The expressions will be equivalent even if a number is substituted for y.
9	D	3(26p − 7 + 14h) and 78p − 21 + 42h are equivalent because if you distribute 3 to 26p − 7 + 14h you will get 78p − 21 + 42h. The expressions will be equivalent even if numbers are substituted for h and p.
10	C	5(6x + 17y − 9z) and 30x + 85y − 45z are equivalent because if you distribute 5 to 6x + 17y − 9z you will get 30x + 85y − 45z. The expressions will be equivalent even if x, y, and z are replaced with numbers.
11	D and E	The distributive property requires that 4 be multiplied by each value in parentheses then those products should be added together.
12	12 y	8y + 8y + 8y = 24y. Therefore given expression = 24y/2 = (24/2)y = 12y.

LumosLearning.com

Equations and Inequalities

Question No.	Answer	Detailed Explanations
1	B	x can be any whole number from 1 to 20, inclusive of 20.
2	A	"17 is less than or equal to" means 17 ≤ "the product of 6 and q" means to multiply 6 and q, or 6q 17 ≤ 6q
3	C	"The quotient of d and 5" means to divide d by 5 "is 15" means "equals 15". $\frac{d}{5} = 15$
4	B	"Three times the quantity u − 4" means to multiply (u−4) by 3 → 3(u−4) "is less than 17" means < 17 3(u−4) < 17
5	D	"The difference between z and the quantity 7 minus r" means to find the difference between z and (7−r), so z − (7−r) "is 54" means equals 54 So, z − (7 − r) = 54
6	A	"The square of the sum of 6 and b" means to square all of (6 + b), or $(6 + b)^2$ "is greater than 10" means "> 10" $(6 + b)^2 > 10$
7	B	"16 less than" means to "subtract 16 from some term" "the product of 5 and h" means to multiply 5 and h or "5h" "is 21" means "equals 21" 5h − 16 = 21
8	C	"8 times the quantity 2x – 7" means to multiply 8 and 2x − 7, which needs to be in parentheses (as a quantity), so 8(2x − 7) "is greater than" means ">" 5 times the quantity 3x + 9" means 5 multiplied by 3x + 9, which needs to be in parentheses (as a quantity), so 5(3x+9) 8(2x − 7) > 5(3x + 9)
9	C	To find how many quarters (or the equivalent of how many quarters) Raul has, you could calculate \$1.50 divided by \$0.25. Then, that amount of quarters would be multiplied by 8, the number of pitches purchased with each quarter. The final expression would read: (\$1.50 ÷ \$0.25) x 8

Question No.	Answer	Detailed Explanations
10	D	Solve to find x: $500 - 3x > 80$ First, subtract 500 from both sides $-3x > -420$ Next, divide both sides by -3. (Don't forget to switch the inequality sign when dividing a negative in an inequality) $x < 140$ So, $x = 120$ would work as a solution. To check: $500 - 3(120) = 500 - 360 = 140$, which is greater than 80.
11	A	5 because 3 x 5 = 15; 15 + 4 is > 17.
12	A, B & C	1, 2, and 4 would complete the equation with a value < 15.

Modeling with Expressions

Question No.	Answer	Detailed Explanations
1	B	Half of 117 can be expressed as (1/2)(117). x less than that is expressed as − x. (1/2)(117) − x.
2	B	Start with $20.00. Then add what he earned mowing the lawn (+c). Then subtract what he spent at the candy store (−x). The expression is $20 + c − x.
3	B	Clinton made a total of 23 items, so you know the expression has to equal 23. He made 6 dessert and 12 appetizers. You do not know how many main courses he made, so that is represented by x. 6 + 12 + x = 23
4	D	Simon read a total of 694 pages. Add the pages from the first book (129), the second book (284) and the third book (y) together. 694 = 129 + 284 + y
5	B	Subtracting the cost of the hat (x) from the total cost ($45.00) would leave the cost of the jeans ($19.00). $45.00 − x = $19.00.
6	B	Janie started with 54 stamps. Giving t stamps away means −t, so 54 − t. Then, Janie gets double t stamps back or + 2t. 54 − t + 2t. Simplified, the expression would be 54 + t.
7	B	The director wants to buy double of x books, which is 2x. Add that to the 2,500 existing books to create the expression 2,500 + 2x.
8	C	The total number of cupcakes is "c." There are 24 boys and 29 girls plus Claire (to make 30). Add all of the people together and equate it to "c." 24 + 30 = c
9	A	Heidi had 172 dolls to start with. She acquired x more so add x to 172. She then acquired 2x more, so add that to 172 also. 172 + x + 2x = 184 Simplify the equation to be: 172 + 3x = 184
10	D	Crystal had 16 plants and each grew 10 tomatoes. To figure out how many tomatoes Crystal had originally, multiply 16 x 10 = 160. Crystal sold x tomatoes, so subtract x from 160. Crystal has 54 tomatoes left. 160 − x = 54
11	C	Answer is 43 > q is the only choice that models a number "greater than" q.
12	B & E	x > 5 and 5 < x

Solving One-Step Problems

Question No.	Answer	Detailed Explanations
1	D	Each time a number from x is multiplied by 8, the product is found in y. So, the equation is y = 8x.
2	D	To find the value of x, you must isolate it. Divide each side by −7. − 7x/−7 = 56/−7. x = −8
3	B	Each value of y is the square of the corresponding x value. This is not a linear relationship.
4	A	$\frac{z}{5} = 20$ To find the value of z, you must isolate it. Multiply each side by 5/1 to cancel out the denominator and isolate the z. z/5 * 5/1 = z 20 * 5/1 = 100 so, z = 100
5	C	$\frac{y}{3} = 12$ To find the value of y, you must isolate it. Multiply by 3 on each side to isolate the y. y/3*(3/1) = 12(3/1) y = 36
6	B	To find the value of p, you must isolate it. Subtract 13 from both sides to isolate the variable. 13 + p − 13 = 39 − 13 p = 26
7	D	To find the value of w, you must isolate it. Divide each side by the coefficient, 6, to isolate the variable. 6w/6 = 54/6 w = 9
8	A	To find the value of x, you must isolate it. Add 4 to both sides. h − 4 = 20 h − 4 + 4 = 20 + 4 h = 24

Question No.	Answer	Detailed Explanations
9	B	To find the value of p, you must first isolate it. Do that by subtracting 72 from both sides. $72 + p - 72 = 108 - 72$ $p = 36$
10	B	To find the value of n, you must isolate it. Subtract 428 from both sides. $428 - n - 428 = 120 - 428$ $-n = -308$ Divide both sides by -1 $n = 308$
11	A	To find the value of m, you must isolate it. Divide both the sides by 4. $4m / 4 = 16 / 4$ $m = 4$
12	A & C	A. $3(6 + k) = 42$ $(3 \times 6) + (3 \times 8) = 42$ $18 + 24 = 42$ C. $8k - 4 = 60$ $8(8) - 4 = 60$ $64 - 4 = 60$

Representing Inequalities

Question No.	Answer	Detailed Explanations
1	A	Half of 12 is 6. Less than 6 caterpillars turned into butterflies. That means that $x < 6$.
2	D	Elliot has at least 5 different favorite foods. That means that he has more than 5 favorite foods. He could have an infinite number of favorite foods because there is no constraint on the number of favorite foods he could have.
3	D	There can be no more than 549 red crayons because that is the maximum number of crayons in the box. You know there are at least 8 red crayons, which means that x is greater than or equal to 8 and less than or equal to 549. $8 \leq x \leq 549$
4	A	"Five times a number" is represented as 5x. "Is greater than" is represented as $>$. "That number minus 17" is represented as $x - 17$. $5x > x - 17$
5	B	"A number divided by 5" is represented as x/5. "Minus five" is represented as $- 5$. "Is less than" is represented as $<$. "Negative four" is represented as -4. $x/5 -5 < -4$
6	C	"A number times six plus three" is represented as $6x + 3$. Three times that is represented as $3(6x + 3)$. "Is less than" is represented as $<$. $3(6x + 3) < 27$
7	B	An open circle means that the number the circle is over is not included in the answer. An arrow pointing to the right means "greater than". The number line would show an open circle over three with an arrow pointing to the right.
8	A	The number of jellybeans that Joey has is represented as x. Amy has three times that many so that is represented as 3x. Together they have at least 44. That means that their jellybeans added together are at least 44, so that is represented as $x + 3x$. At least means that they could have 44 or more than 44 so that is represented as $\geq$ $x + 3x \geq 44$

LumosLearning.com

Question No.	Answer	Detailed Explanations
9	C	The number of cases that Sandra has is represented as x. The 8 more she gets is represented as x + 8. She has more than 29, so that is represented as > 29 x + 8 > 29
10	C	The number of bees in each hive is represented as x. There are the same number of bees in all 25 beehives. The total number of bees is represented as 25x. The total number of bees on the farm is greater than 800. Greater than is represented as > 800. 25x > 800
11	A	Closed circle represents "Greater than or equal to" or "less than or equal to" on the number line. An arrow to the right represents "greater than". Answer is $x \geq 18$.
12	E	Closed circle represents "Greater than or equal to" or "less than or equal to" on the number line. An arrow to the left represents "less than". $x \leq -15$
13		Nami is correct, the sign is wrong. To be at least 13 years old means to be 13 years old or older. Hence the correct inequality symbol is $\geq$ and not $\leq$. The arrow points toward the smaller number. In this case the smaller number is 13.
14		"A number" is represented as x. "Divided by 5" is represented as $\frac{x}{5}$. "Is at most" means that it could be -23 or less than -23, so that is represented as $\leq$ $\frac{x}{5} \leq -23$

Quantitative Relationships

Question No.	Answer	Detailed Explanations
1	B	"m" represents the amount of money that Logan needs. "p" represents the number of pounds that Logan buys. The amount of money Logan needs is found by multiplying the cost of the candy by the number of pounds that Logan buys. m = 0.79(p)
2	B	m = $0.84(3) m = $2.52
3	A	"t" represents the total amount Norman spent. "g" represents the number of gallons that Norman purchased. To find the total amount that Norman spent, multiply the price of the gas by the total number of gallons that Norman purchased. t = g(3.55)
4	D	t = 13 gallons ($3.58) t = 13(3.58) t = 46.54 $46.54
5	C	"b" represents the number of bottles of lemonade "o" represents the total number of ounces of lemonade To find out the total number of ounces of lemonade that Penny purchased, multiply the number of bottles (b) by the number of ounces in each bottle, 60. 60(b) = o
6	B	"t" represents the total number of minutes Ethan played "g" represents the number of games "m" represent the number of minutes in each game To find out the total number of minutes Ethan played, multiply the number of games by the number of minutes in each game. t = g(m)
7	D	The equation t = c(n) can be used with any numbers. The equation has the number of trees and the cost of one tree as variables. Those quantities, no matter what they are, when multiplied together will always equal the total cost.
8	A	"c" represents the total cost "b" represents the number of bouquets "f" represents the number of sunflowers To find the total cost, multiply the number of bouquets by the number of sunflowers by the price of the sunflowers. c = 3(bf)

Question No.	Answer	Detailed Explanations
9	A	c = 3(bf) c = 3(6)(5) c = 90 $90
10	C	The number of eggs that Hen B lays depends on the number of eggs that Hen A lays. Hen B lays 4 times more than Hen A. That is represented as 4a b = 4a

11	B & C	B. 100 balloons equal 10 packs of 10
		    $2.50 x 10 quantity = $25.00
		
		C. 30 balloons equal 3 packs of 10
		    $2.50 x 3 = $7.50

12		(see table and work below)

Day	Money Spent on Sodas	Sodas Purchased	Price per Soda
Monday	$30.00	24	$1.25
Wednesday	$57.50	46	$1.25
Friday	$41.25	33	$1.25

m = $30.00
24 x $1.25 = $30
w = 46 sodas
$57.50 / $1.25 = 46
f = 33 sodas
$41.25/ $1.25 = 33

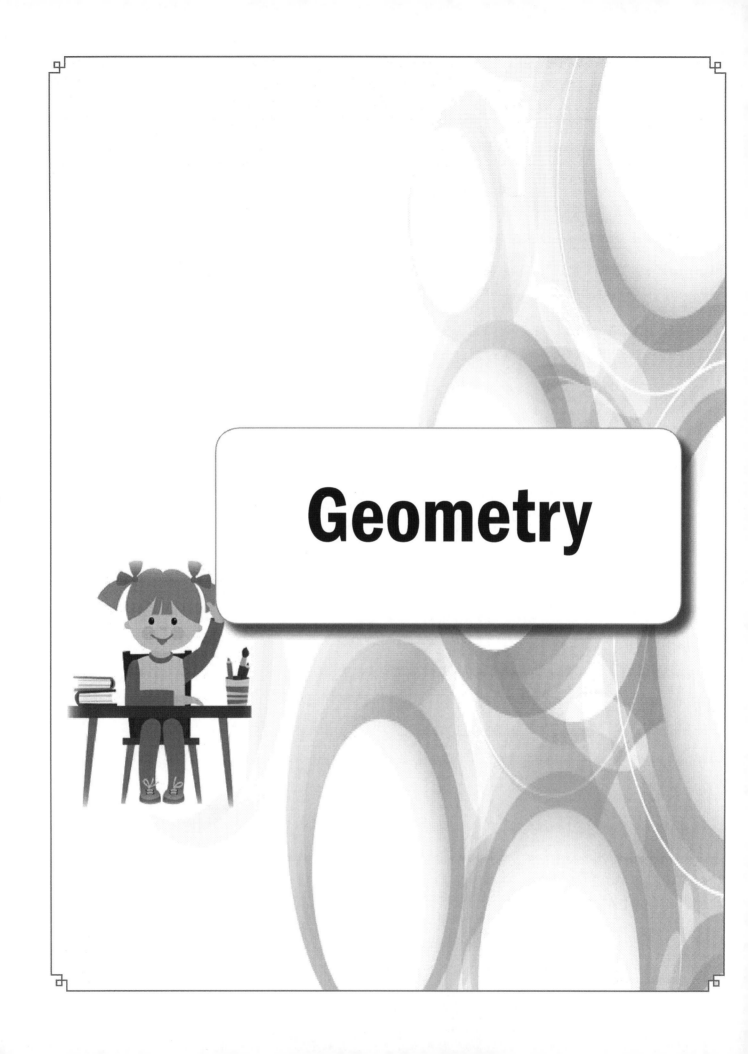

Geometry

Area

1. What is the area of the figure below?

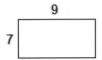

- Ⓐ 16 square units
- Ⓑ 63 square units
- Ⓒ 32 square units
- Ⓓ 45 square units

2. What is the area of the figure below?

- Ⓐ 12 square units
- Ⓑ 24 square units
- Ⓒ 18 square units
- Ⓓ 36 square units

3. What is the area of the figure below? (Assume that the vertical height of the parallelogram is 3 units .)

- Ⓐ 28 square units
- Ⓑ 12 square units
- Ⓒ 14 square units
- Ⓓ 21 square units

4. The figure shows a small square inside a larger square. What is the area of the shaded portion of the figure below?

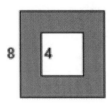

   Ⓐ 64 square units
   Ⓑ 48 square units
   Ⓒ 16 square units
   Ⓓ 80 square units

5. What is the area of the circle shown below? Round to the nearest tenth. (Let π = 3.14)

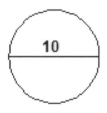

   Ⓐ 78.5 square units
   Ⓑ 314 square units
   Ⓒ 15.7 square units
   Ⓓ 31.4 square units

6. What is the area of the figure below? (Assume that the vertical height of the triangle is 2.8 units)

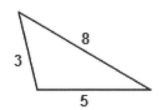

   Ⓐ 15 square units
   Ⓑ 7 square units
   Ⓒ 14 square units
   Ⓓ 40 square units

7. What is the area of the gray portion of the figure below? The larger circle has a diameter of 24, and the smaller circle has a diameter of 12. (Let the value of π be 3.14.) Round to the nearest hundredth.

Ⓐ 452.16 square units
Ⓑ 339.12 square units
Ⓒ 113.04 square units
Ⓓ 1,356.48 square units

8. What is the area of the shaded part of the figure below? The radius of the larger circle is 10 and the radius of the smaller circle is 5. (Let the value of π be 3.14.) Round to the nearest tenth.

Ⓐ 314.0 square units
Ⓑ 157.0 square units
Ⓒ 31.4 square units
Ⓓ 235.5 square units

9. What is the area of the gray part of the squares below?.

Ⓐ 289 square units
Ⓑ 81 square units
Ⓒ 208 square units
Ⓓ 370 square units

10. **What is the area of a triangle with a base of 20 feet and a vertical height of 40 feet?**

    Ⓐ A = 200 square ft.
    Ⓑ A = 800 square ft.
    Ⓒ A = 400 square ft.
    Ⓓ A = 600 square ft.

11. **Calculate the area of the triangle shown below and write the answer in the box.**

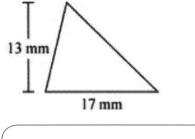

    mm²

12. **Calculate the area of the triangle shown. Write the answer in the box given below.**

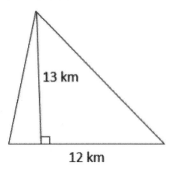

    km²

13. **George and Maggie were completing their homework together. One problem asked to find the area of a triangle. Below are George's and Maggie's work.**

George's Work

$A = \dfrac{bh}{2}$

$A = \dfrac{(3.2)(4.5)}{2}$

$A = \dfrac{14.4}{2}$

$A = 7.2 \text{ mm}^2$

Maggie's Work

$A = \dfrac{bh}{2}$

$A = \dfrac{(3.2)(3.8)}{2}$

$A = \dfrac{12.16}{2}$

$A = 6.08 \text{ mm}^2$

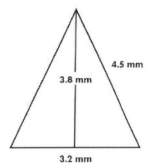

4.5 mm

3.8 mm

3.2 mm

Whose answer is correct? Explain your reasoning.

Online Resources: Area

URL	QR Code
http://lumoslearning.com/a/m15261	

 Videos   Apps   Sample Questions

NOTES

Surface Area and Volume

1. **How many rectangular faces would a trapezoidal prism have?**

   Ⓐ two
   Ⓑ four
   Ⓒ six
   Ⓓ zero

2. **Which of the following statements is true of a rhombus?**

   Ⓐ A rhombus is a parallelogram.
   Ⓑ A rhombus is a quadrilateral.
   Ⓒ A rhombus is equilateral.
   Ⓓ All of the above are true.

3. **A cube has a volume of 1,000 cm³. What is its surface area?**

   Ⓐ 100 square cm
   Ⓑ 60 square cm
   Ⓒ 600 square cm
   Ⓓ It cannot be determined.

4. **A solid figure is casting a square shadow. The figure could <u>not</u> be a _____.**

   Ⓐ rectangular prism
   Ⓑ cylinder
   Ⓒ pentagonal pyramid
   Ⓓ hexagonal prism

5. **Which of the following solid figures has the most flat surfaces?**

   Ⓐ a cube
   Ⓑ a triangular prism
   Ⓒ a hexagonal prism
   Ⓓ a pentagonal pyramid

6. **Calculate the surface area of the box shown below.**

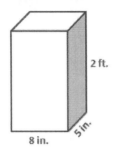

2 ft.

5 in.

8 in.

Ⓐ 132 square inches
Ⓑ 80 square inches
Ⓒ 704 square inches
Ⓓ 352 square inches

7. **Complete the following statement.**
   A hexagon must have _____.

   Ⓐ 6 sides and 6 angles
   Ⓑ 8 sides and 8 angles
   Ⓒ 10 sides and 10 angles
   Ⓓ 7 sides and 7 angles

8. **A single marble tile measures 25 cm by 20 cm. How many tiles will be required to cover a floor with dimensions 2 meters by 3 meters?**

   Ⓐ 320 tiles
   Ⓑ 240 tiles
   Ⓒ 180 tiles
   Ⓓ 120 tiles

9. **Calculate the volume of the box shown below.**

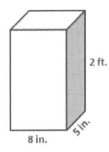

2 ft.

8 in.

5 in.

Ⓐ 80 cubic inches
Ⓑ 960 cubic inches
Ⓒ 800 cubic inches
Ⓓ None of the above

10. **What is the surface area of a rectangular box with dimensions 4 cm, 6 cm, and 10 cm?**

Ⓐ 248 square cm
Ⓑ 240 square cm
Ⓒ 124 square cm
Ⓓ 224 square cm

11. **What is the volume of a rectangular prism that has a length of 10 cm, a width of 5 cm, and a height of 2 cm? Circle the correct answer choice.**

Ⓐ V = 50 cubic cm
Ⓑ V = 17 cubic cm
Ⓒ V = 10 cubic cm
Ⓓ V = 100 cubic cm

Name: _____   Date: _____

12. Determine the volume of the prism shown. Write your answer in the box given below.

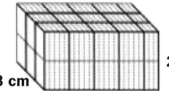

cm³

Online Resources: Surface Area and Volume

URL	QR Code
http://lumoslearning.com/a/m15262	

 Videos   Apps   Sample Questions

NOTES

Coordinate Geometry

1. **The points A (0, 0), B (5, 0), C (6, 2), D (5, 5), and E (0, 5) are plotted in a coordinate grid. Describe the angles in pentagon ABCDE.**

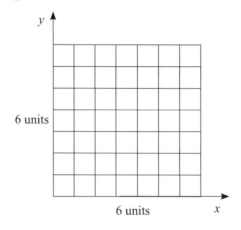

   Ⓐ 2 right angles and 3 obtuse angles
   Ⓑ 2 right angles, 2 obtuse angles, and 1 acute angle
   Ⓒ 3 right angles and 2 obtuse angles
   Ⓓ 2 right angles, 2 acute angles, and 1 obtuse angle

2. **The corners of a shape are located at (1,2), (5,2), (2,3) and (4,3) in a coordinate grid. What type of shape is it?**

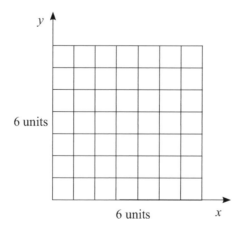

   Ⓐ square
   Ⓑ parallelogram
   Ⓒ rhombus
   Ⓓ trapezoid

3. **Which of the following graphs shows a 180-degree clockwise rotation about the origin?**

Ⓐ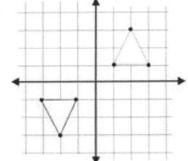

Ⓒ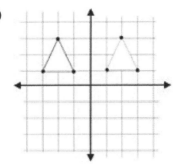

Ⓑ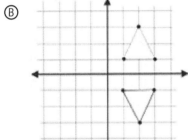

Ⓓ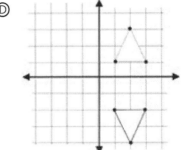

4. **Identify the point on the grid below that corresponds to the ordered pair of x = 2y + 3, when y = 2.**

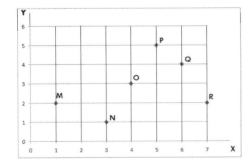

Ⓐ Point M
Ⓑ Point N
Ⓒ Point R
Ⓓ Point Q

5. **What figure is formed when you draw straight line segments between the following points (in the order they are listed)? (2, −13), (2, 1), (8, 1), (8, 5), (2, 5), (2, 10), (−2, 10), (−2, 5), (−8, 5), (−8, 1), (−2, 1), (−2, −13)**

Ⓐ star
Ⓑ cross
Ⓒ heart
Ⓓ boat

6. **You are looking for a point on the line: y = 10 − 2x. You know that x = −1. What does y equal?**

Ⓐ 10
Ⓑ 8
Ⓒ 12
Ⓓ −2

7. **Assume a function has the rule y = 2x. Which grid shows the ordered pair formed when x = 3?**

Ⓐ
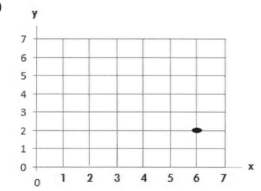

Ⓒ
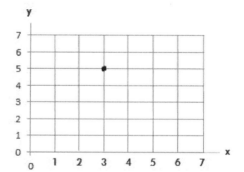

Ⓑ
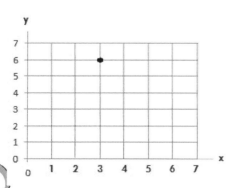

Ⓓ None of the above

8. **Which equation matches this graph?**

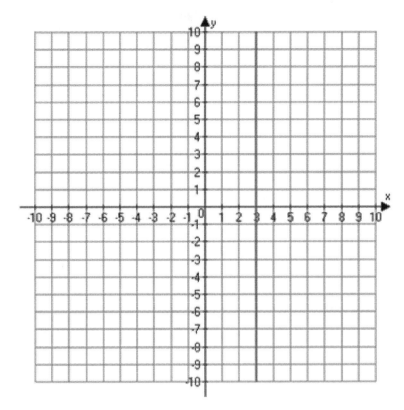

- Ⓐ y = 3
- Ⓑ x = 3
- Ⓒ y = 0
- Ⓓ x = −3

9. **What ordered pair would fit in this equation?**

    y = x − 3

- Ⓐ (4, 0)
- Ⓑ (0, 4)
- Ⓒ (4, 1)
- Ⓓ (1, 4)

11. What is the area of this polygon? Write your answer in the box given below.

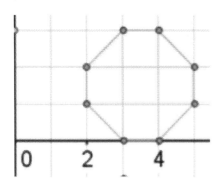

square units

12. What is the area of the rectangle. Write your answer in the box given below.

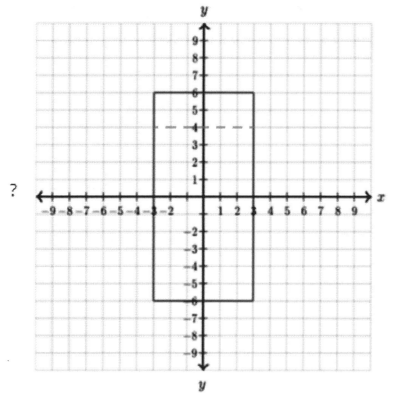

_____ **square units**

Online Resources: Coordinate Geometry

URL	QR Code
http://lumoslearning.com/a/m15263	

 Videos   Apps   Sample Questions

NOTES

Nets

1. **Identify the solid given its net:**

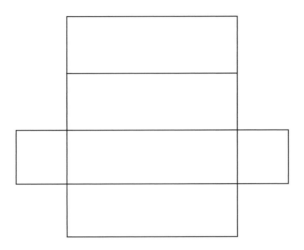

    Ⓐ Rectangular prism
    Ⓑ Cube
    Ⓒ Triangular prism
    Ⓓ Sphere

2. **Identify the solid given its net:**

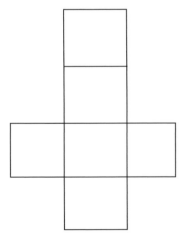

    Ⓐ Cube
    Ⓑ Sphere
    Ⓒ Rectangular prism
    Ⓓ Square pyramid

3. **Identify the solid given its net:**

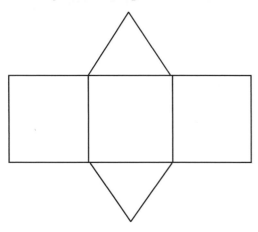

   Ⓐ Rectangular prism
   Ⓑ Cube
   Ⓒ Triangular prism
   Ⓓ Sphere

4. **Identify the solid given its net:**

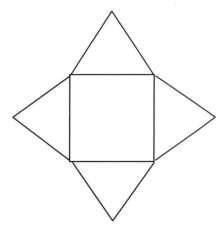

   Ⓐ Cube
   Ⓑ Sphere
   Ⓒ Rectangular prism
   Ⓓ Square pyramid

5. **Identify the solid given its net:**

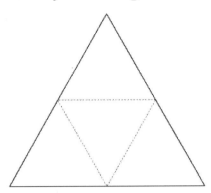

 Ⓐ Cube
 Ⓑ Sphere
 Ⓒ Rectangular prism
 Ⓓ Triangular pyramid

6. **Identify the solid given its net:**

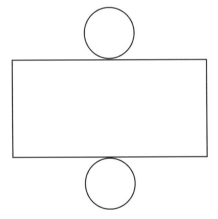

 Ⓐ Cube
 Ⓑ Sphere
 Ⓒ Cylinder
 Ⓓ Square pyramid

7. **Identify the solid given its net:**

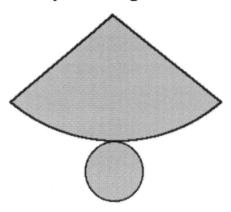

   Ⓐ Cube
   Ⓑ Cone
   Ⓒ Cylinder
   Ⓓ Square pyramid

8. **The diagram below represents the net of a solid figure. Find the surface area given L = 4 in, W = 4 in, H = 12 in.**

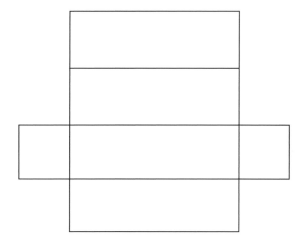

   Ⓐ 228 square ft.
   Ⓑ 224 square in.
   Ⓒ 448 square in.
   Ⓓ 112 square in.

9. Identify the solid, given its net:

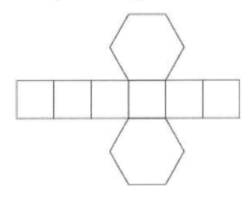

Ⓐ Sphere
Ⓑ Cone
Ⓒ Hexagonal prism
Ⓓ Hexagonal pyramid

10. Identify the number of faces, edges and vertices in a rectangular pyramid.

Ⓐ Faces = 5, Vertices = 6, Edges = 9
Ⓑ Faces = 4, Vertices = 4, Edges = 6
Ⓒ Faces = 6, Vertices = 8, Edges = 12
Ⓓ Faces = 5, Vertices = 5, Edges = 8

11. Use a net or formula to find the surface area of the figure. The length is 5, the width is 4 and the height is 2. Write your answer in the box given below.

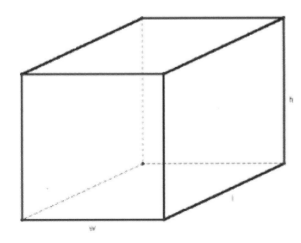

11. **Use a net or formula to find the surface area of the figure. The length is 5, the width is 4 and the height is 2. Write your answer in the box given below.**

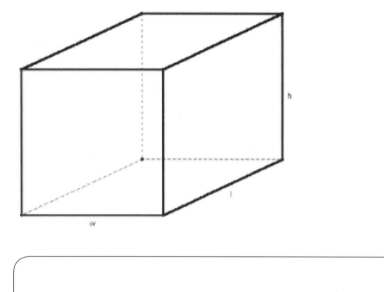

12. **Use a net or formula to find the surface area of the figure. Length is 2, width is 3, and height is 4. Circle the correct answer choice.**

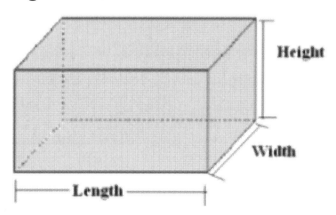

Ⓐ 52 square units
Ⓑ 42 square units
Ⓒ 32 square units
Ⓓ 22 square units

13. Identify the number of faces, edges and vertices in a hexagonal prism. Circle the correct answer choice.

Ⓐ Faces = 8, Vertices = 10, Edges = 16
Ⓑ Faces = 8, Vertices = 12, Edges = 20
Ⓒ Faces = 8, Vertices = 12, Edges = 18
Ⓓ Faces = 8, Vertices = 10, Edges = 18

Online Resources: Nets

URL	QR Code
http://lumoslearning.com/a/m15264	

📹 Videos   📱 Apps   📖 Sample Questions

End of Geometry

NOTES

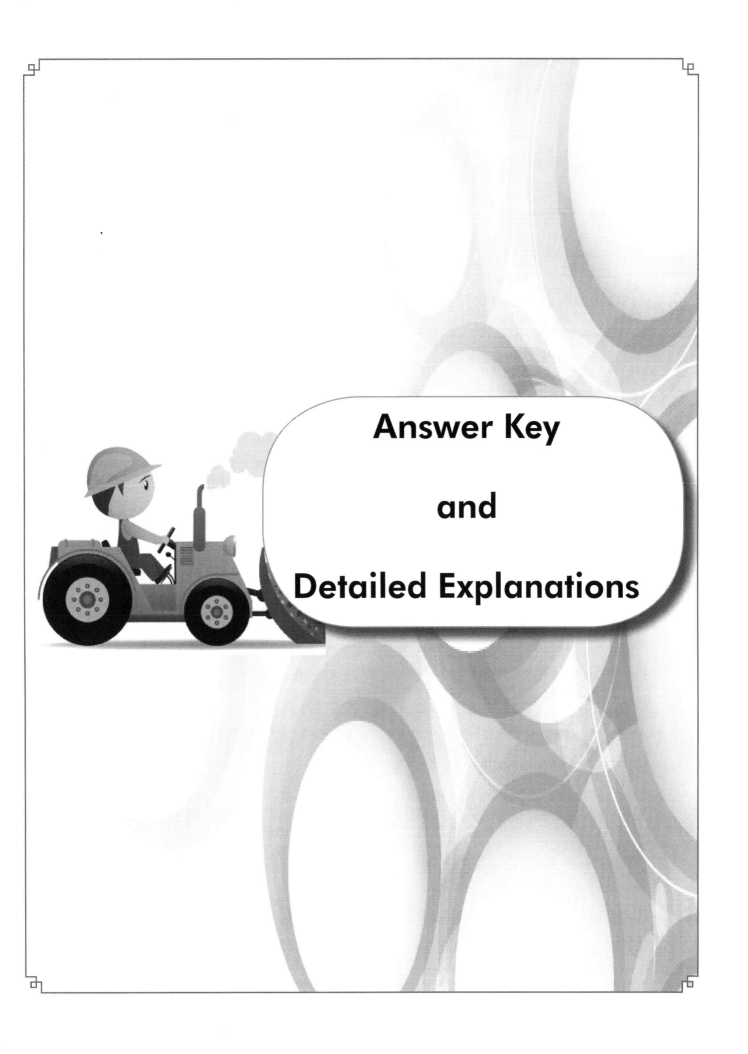

Answer Key

and

Detailed Explanations

Question No.	Answer	Detailed Explanations
1	B	Area of a rectangle = length x width. A = 9 x 7 A = 63 units^2
2	D	Area of a square = (length of side)^2. A = 6^2 A = 36 units^2
3	D	Area of a parallelogram = base x height. A = 7 x 3 A = 21 units^2
4	B	First find the area of the larger square. Then find the area of the smaller square. Use the formula: A = (length of side)^2 to find the area of both squares. $A_{large} = 8 \times 8 = 64$ $A_{small} = 4 \times 4 = 16$ Subtract the area of the smaller square from the larger square to find the area of the shaded portion (64 − 16 = 48).
5	C	Area of a square A = (length of side)^2 A = 7 x 7 A = 49 units^2
6	B	Area of a triangle = (1/2)bh A = ($\frac{1}{2}$) (5*2.8) A = ($\frac{1}{2}$) (14) A = 7 units^2
7	A	A = bh A = 5 x 12 A = 60 units^2
8	D	A = bh (where h is the vertical height of the parallelogram) A = 19 x 6 A = 114 units^2
9	C	Area of a square = (length of side)^2 Area of the larger square is 17*17 = 289 units^2 Area of the smaller square is 9*9 = 81 units^2 To find the area of the shaded portion, subtract the area of the smaller square from the area of the larger square: 289 − 81 = 208

Question No.	Answer	Detailed Explanations
10	C	The formula for the area of a triangle is: $A = (\frac{1}{2})bh$ $a = (\frac{1}{2})(20)(40)$ $a = (\frac{1}{2})(800)$ $a = 400$ sq. ft.
11	110.5 mm^2	For a triangle, Area = ½ (base x height) b = 17 mm h = 13 mm So, ½ (17 x 13) = area ½ (221) = 110.5 mm^2
12	78 km^2	Area = ½ (base x height) b = 12 km h = 13 km So, ½ (12 x 13) = area ½ (156) = 78 km^2
13		Maggie's answer is correct. The height of a triangle is perpendicular to its base. George used the side of the triangle as the triangle's height but the side is not perpendicular to the base of 3.2mm. Maggie, however, did use the height, which is 3.8 mm, as it is perpendicular to the base.

Surface Area and Volume

Question No.	Answer	Detailed Explanations
1	B	A prism has rectangular faces connecting the two bases. A trapezoid has four sides, so four rectangular faces are on a trapezoidal prism.
2	D	A rhombus is a parallelogram that is a quadrilateral and is equilateral.
3	C	Since the volume of a cube is found using the formula: $V = $ (side length)^3, the length of each side of this cube would be 10 [$V = (10)(10)(10)$]. The surface area of a cube is found by finding the area of one face: $A = $ (side)^2, then multiplying by 6, since there are 6 faces, so 6(side)^2. $6(10)^2 = 6(10)(10) = 6(100) = 600$
4	C	A pentagonal prism has 5 sides so it would not cast a square shadow.
5	C	A hexagonal prism would have a total of 8 faces. A cube has 6, a triagular prism has 5, and a pentagonal pyramid has 6.
6	C	First convert 2 feet to inches. There are 12 inches per foot so 2 feet is $12 * 2 = 24$ inches. The given figure is a cuboid or a rectangular prism which has six rectangular surfaces. Area of a rectangle = length x breadth. Therefore total S.A. $= 2(L_1 W_1) + 2(L_2 W_2) + 2(L_3 W_3)$ where $L_1 W_1$ are the dimensions of the top and bottom faces of the prism; $L_2 W_2$ are the dimensions of the front and back faces of the prism and $L_3 W_3$ are the dimensions of the side faces of the prism. Replace the variables with the appropriate values: S.A. $= 2(5*8) + 2(8*24) + 2(5*24)$ S.A. $= 2(40) + 2(192) + 2(120)$ S.A. $= 80 + 384 + 240$ S.A. $= 704$ square inches
7	A	A hexagon is a shape with 6 angles and 6 sides.
8	D	First, convert meters into centimeters to standardize the measurement units. 1 meter = 100 centimeters, so 2 meters = 200 centimeters and 3 meters = 300 centimeters. To find how many tiles will be needed across, divide $\frac{300}{25} = 12$ To find how many tiles will be needed down, divide $\frac{200}{20} = 10$ Then multiply the number of tiles needed across the floor by the number of times needed down the floor. $12*10 = 120$ tiles.

Question No.	Answer	Detailed Explanations
9	B	To find the volume of a rectangular prism, use the following formula: $V = LWH$ Substitute the appropriate values for the variables. Then simplify. First convert 2 feet to inches. There are 12 inches per foot so 2 feet is $12 * 2 = 24$ inches. $V = (8)(5)(24)$ $V = (40)(24)$ $V = 960$ cubic inches
10	A	To find the surface area, use the following formula: $S.A. = 2(L_1W_1) + 2(L_2W_2) + 2(L_3W_3)$ Where L_1W_1 represent the top and bottom of the prism L_2W_2 represent the front and back faces of the prism L_3W_3 represent the side faces of the prism. Replace the variables with the appropriate values: $S.A. = 2(4*6) + 2(4*10) + 2(6*10)$ $S.A. = 2(24) + 2(40) + 2(60)$ $S.A. = 48 + 80 + 120$ $S.A. = 248$ sq. cm.
11	D	$V = LWH$ $V = (10)(5)(2)$ $V = 50(2)$ $V = 100$ cubic cm
12	$27\frac{3}{5}$ cm³	$V = lwh$ cm³ $= (4\frac{3}{5})(3)(2)$ $V = (\frac{23}{5})(3)(2)$ $V = \frac{23 \times 3 \times 2}{5} = \frac{138}{5} = 27\frac{3}{5}$ cm³

Coordinate Geometry

Question No.	Answer	Detailed Explanations
1	A	When the points are connected, Angles A and E are right angles and Angles B, C, and D are all obtuse angles.
2	D	When the points are correctly connected, a trapezoid is created.
3	A	A 180-degree clockwise rotation about the origin will cause the top of the triangle to point to the bottom, and also the shape to shift from Quadrant I to Quadrant III.
4	C	$x = 2y + 3$, when $y = 2$ Substitute 2 for y. $x = 2(2) + 3$ $x = 4 + 3$ $x = 7$ This makes the ordered pair (7,2), which corresponds to point R.
5	B	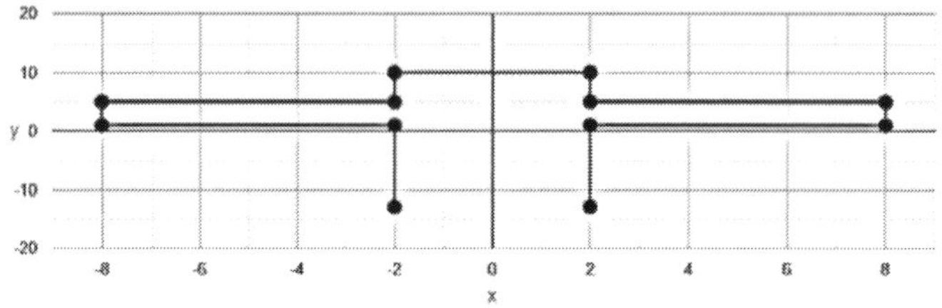 When all points are correctly plotted, a cross is formed.
6	C	To determine the value of y, substitute the given value of x into the equation. $y = 10 - 2x$. If $x = -1$, then $y = 10 - 2(-1)$ $y = 10 - (-2)$ $y = 12$
7	B	To determine the value of y, substitute the given value of x into the equation. $y = 2x$. If $x = 3$, then $y = 2(3)$ $y = 6$ giving you the coordinate (3,6)
8	B	The equation, $x = 3$, will match the graph above, because for any given y coordinates, x will always be 3.

Question No.	Answer	Detailed Explanation
9	C	To determine what ordered pair would fit, substitute each x-coordinate and solve for the y-coordinate. A) (4, 0): x=4 so $y = 4 - 3 = 1$; The y-coordinate is 0 not 1 so this ordered pair does not fit. B) (0, 4): x=0 so $y = 0 - 3 = -3$; The y-coordinate is 4 not -3 so this ordered pair does not fit. C) (4,1): x=4 so $y = 4 - 3 = 1$; since the y-coordinate is also 1 this ordered pair fits. D) (1, 4): x=4 so $y = 1 - 3 = -2$; The y-coordinate is 4 not -2 so this ordered pair does not fit. Answer C is the only ordered pair that fits.
10	C	The Quadrants move counter clockwise from I to IV. The upper left region would be Quadrant II.
11	7 square units.	7 square units. There are 5 whole square units. There are 4 units that are right triangles, for a total of 2 whole squares. $5 + 2 = 7$ square units.
12	72 square units	72 square units. 6 units along the x-axis multiplied by 12 units along the y-axis equals. 72 total square units.

Nets

Question No.	Answer	Detailed Explanations
1	A	When the exposed edges are connected a rectangular prism will be formed.
2	A	When the exposed edges are connected a cube will be formed.
3	C	When the exposed edges are connected a triangular prism will be formed.
4	D	When the exposed edges are connected a square pyramid will be formed.
5	D	When the exposed edges are connected a triangular pyramid will be formed.
6	C	When the exposed edges are connected a cylinder will be formed.
7	B	When the exposed edges are connected a cone will be formed.
8	B	This net represents a rectangular prism. The surface area of a rectangular prism = $2(l*w + l*h + w*h)$ $= 2(4*4 + 4*12 + 4*12)$ $= 2(16 + 48 + 48)$ $= 2(112)$ $= 224$ square in.
9	C	The hexagon ends, attached by six rectangular faces, create a hexagonal prism.
10	D	 There are 5 faces, 5 vertices, and 8 edges in a rectangular pyramid.
11	C	To find the surface area, find the area of each side using the net S.A. $= (5*4) + (5*4) + (4*2) + (4*2) + (5*2) + (5*2) =$ $= 20 + 20 + 8 + 8 + 10 + 10$ $= 76$ square units

Question No.	Answer	Detailed Explanations
12	A	Find the area of each face and add all the areas together in order to find the surface area: (2*3) + (2*3) + (3*4) + (3*4) + (2*4) + (2*4) = 52 units^2
13	C	There are 8 faces, 12 vertices, and 18 edges in a hexagonal prism.

NOTES

Additional Information

What if I buy more than one Lumos Study Program?

Step 1
Visit the URL and login to your account.
http://www.lumoslearning.com

Step 2
Click on 'My tedBooks' under the "Account" tab.
Place the Book Access Code and submit.

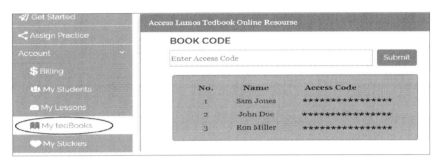

Step 3
To add the new book for a registered student, choose the
⊙ Existing Student button and select the student and submit.

To add the new book for a new student, choose the ⊙ Add New student
button and complete the student registration.

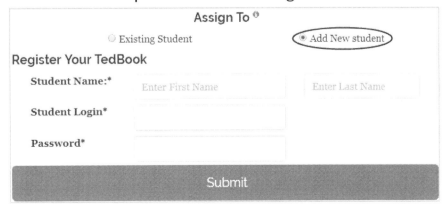

Lumos StepUp® Mobile App FAQ For Students

What is the Lumos StepUp® App?

It is a FREE application you can download onto your Android Smartphones, tablets, iPhones, and iPads.

What are the Benefits of the StepUp® App?

This mobile application gives convenient access to Practice Tests, Common Core State Standards, Online Workbooks, and learning resources through your Smartphone and tablet computers.

- Eleven Technology enhanced question types in both MATH and ELA
- Sample questions for Arithmetic drills
- Standard specific sample questions
- Instant access to the Common Core State Standards
- Jokes and cartoons to make learning fun!

Do I Need the StepUp® App to Access Online Workbooks?

No, you can access Lumos StepUp® Online Workbooks through a personal computer. The StepUp® app simply enhances your learning experience and allows you to conveniently access StepUp® Online Workbooks and additional resources through your smart phone or tablet.

How can I Download the App?

Visit **lumoslearning.com/a/stepup-app** using your Smartphone or tablet and follow the instructions to download the app.

**QR Code
for Smartphone
Or Tablet Users**

Lumos StepUp® Mobile App FAQ
For Parents and Teachers

What is the Lumos StepUp® App?

It is a free app that teachers can use to easily access real-time student activity information as well as assign learning resources to students. Parents can also use it to easily access school-related information such as homework assigned by teachers and PTA meetings. It can be downloaded onto smart phones and tablets from popular App Stores.

What are the Benefits of the Lumos StepUp® App?

It provides convenient access to

- Standards aligned learning resources for your students
- An easy to use Dashboard
- Student progress reports
- Active and inactive students in your classroom
- Professional development information
- Educational Blogs

How can I Download the App?

Visit **lumoslearning.com/a/stepup-app** using your Smartphone or tablet and follow the instructions to download the app.

**QR Code
for Smartphone
Or Tablet Users**

Common Core Standards Cross-reference Table

CCSS	Standard Description	Page No.	Question No.
6.EE.A.1	Write and evaluate numerical expressions involving whole-number exponents.	4	1 to 12
6.EE.A.2	Write, read, and evaluate expressions in which letters stand for numbers.	8	1 to 12
6.EE.A.2.B	Identify parts of an expression using mathematical terms (sum, term, product, factor, quotient, coefficient); view one or more parts of an expression as a single entity. For example, describe the expression 2 (8 + 7) as a product of two factors; view (8 + 7) as both a single entity and a sum of two terms.	12	1 to 12
6.EE.A.2.C	Evaluate expressions at specific values of their variables. Include expressions that arise from formulas used in real-world problems. Perform arithmetic operations, including those involving whole-number exponents, in the conventional order when there are no parentheses to specify a particular order (Order of Operations). For example, use the formulas $V = s3$ and $A = 6 s2$ to find the volume and surface area of a cube with sides of length s = 1/2.	16	1 to 12
6.EE.A.3	Apply the properties of operations to generate equivalent expressions. For example, apply the distributive property to the expression 3 (2 + x) to produce the equivalent expression 6 + 3x; apply the distributive property to the expression 24x + 18y to produce the equivalent expression 6 (4x + 3y); apply properties of operations to y + y + y to produce the equivalent expression 3y.	21	1 to 12
6.EE.A.4	Identify when two expressions are equivalent (i.e., when the two expressions name the same number regardless of which value is substituted into them). For example, the expressions y + y + y and 3y are equivalent because they name the same number regardless of which number y stands for.	25	1 to 12
6.EE.B.5	Understand solving an equation or inequality as a process of answering a question: which values from a specified set, if any, make the equation or inequality true? Use substitution to determine whether a given number in a specified set makes an equation or inequality true.	29	1 to 12

CCSS	Standard Description	Page No.	Question No.
6.EE.B.6	Use variables to represent numbers and write expressions when solving a real-world or mathematical problem; understand that a variable can represent an unknown number, or, depending on the purpose at hand, any number in a specified set.	33	1 to 12
6.EE.B.7	Solve real-world and mathematical problems by writing and solving equations of the form x + p = q and px = q for cases in which p, q and x are all nonnegative rational numbers.	37	1 to 12
6.EE.B.8	Write an inequality of the form x > c or x < c to represent a constraint or condition in a real-world or mathematical problem. Recognize that inequalities of the form x > c or x < c have infinitely many solutions; represent solutions of such inequalities on number line diagrams.	47	1 to 14
6.EE.C.9	Use variables to represent two quantities in a real-world problem that change in relationship to one another; write an equation to express one quantity, thought of as the dependent variable, in terms of the other quantity, thought of as the independent variable. Analyze the relationship between the dependent and independent variables using graphs and tables, and relate these to the equation. For example, in a problem involving motion at constant speed, list and graph ordered pairs of distances and times, and write the equation d = 65t to represent the relationship between distance and time.	70	1 to 12
6.G.A.1	Find the area of right triangles, other triangles, special quadrilaterals, and polygons by composing into rectangles or decomposing into triangles and other shapes; apply these techniques in the context of solving real-world and mathematical problems.	71	1 to 13
6.G.A.2	Find the volume of a right rectangular prism with fractional edge lengths by packing it with unit cubes of the appropriate unit fraction edge lengths, and show that the volume is the same as would be found by multiplying the edge lengths of the prism. Apply the formulas V = l w h and V = b h to find volumes of right rectangular prisms with fractional edge lengths in the context of solving real-world and mathematical problems.	77	1 to 12

CCSS	Standard Description	Page No.	Question No.
6.G.A.3	Draw polygons in the coordinate plane given coordinates for the vertices; use coordinates to find the length of a side joining points with the same first coordinate or the same second coordinate. Apply these techniques in the context of solving real-world and mathematical problems.	82	1 to 12
6.G.A.4	Represent three-dimensional figures using nets made up of rectangles and triangles, and use the nets to find the surface area of these figures. Apply these techniques in the context of solving real-world and mathematical problems	89	1 to 13

 **lumos learning**
Developed by Expert Teachers

Test Prep and Smart Homework Help

Lumos StepUp is a unique e-Learning program that provides online resources along with personalized coaching to help improve student achievement.

 Practice Assessments that mirror standardized Tests

 Parent Portal: Review online work of your child

 Individualized homework assistance (StepUp® Coach™)

 Student Portal: Anywhere access to Learning Resources

 15 Master Tech Enhanced Question Types

 Discover Educational Apps, Books, and Videos

Subscribe Now ▶

 888-309-8227

 www.lumoslearning.com/stepup

School Supplemental Program

COMPUTER-BASED SKILLS PRACTICE
AND ASSESSMENT REHEARSAL

- ➤ Standards-aligned workbooks

- ➤ Practice tests that mirror state assessments

- ➤ Fifteen tech-enhanced items practice

- ➤ Resource recommendations such as apps, books, & videos

- ➤ Personalized learning assignments for students

Call us for more information

888 - 309 - 8227

lumoslearning.com/a/online-program

Trusted by over 60,000 Students, 600 Schools, & 6000 Teachers

PARTIAL CUSTOMER LIST

Other Books in SkillBuilder Series

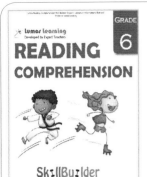

Reading Comprehension SkillBuilder

- Literature
- Informational Text
- Evidence-based Reading

English Language and Grammar SkillBuilder

- Conventions
- Vocabulary
- Knowledge of Language

Ratios & Proportional Relationships and The Number System SkillBuilder

- Unit Rates
- Measurement
- Division of Whole Numbers

Statistics and Probability SkillBuilder

- Distribution
- Graphs
- Charts

http://lumoslearning.com/a/sbtb

Made in the USA
Columbia, SC
23 January 2022

54685586R00067